Changing Addresses

Contemporary Austrian Writing

Johann Holzner and Alois Hotschnig, Editors

Brigitte Scott, Translator

STUDIES IN CENTRAL EUROPEAN HISTORY CULTURE & LITERATURE

Printed in the United States of America.

Changing Addresses: Contemporary Austrian Writing

Library of Congress Control Number: 2011940385

Book design by Lauren Capone

*i*up

innsbruck university press

European ISBN: 978-3-902811-43-1

University of New Orleans Press

US ISBN: 978-160801-081-3

**Studies in Central European History,
Literature and Culture**

Günter Bischof, Series Editor

Contents

Preface

The almost 30-year old partnership between the University of Innsbruck and the University of New Orleans is unique in the density of its activities and wealth of intellectual cross-fertilization. Through the auspices of this model university partnership, thousands of students have received the opportunity to study overseas, dozens of faculty members have been exchanged, and regular academic symposia and conferences have been organized and published. The journal *Contemporary Austrian Studies* is in its 21st year and is now published jointly by the University of New Orleans (UNO) Press and *innsbruck* university press (*i*up). The publication of this selection of contemporary Austrian writing takes the cooperation between these two university presses a step further and onto another level. This volume of contemporary Austrian literature was first published by *i*up under the heading of *Wechselnde Anschriften* (2008). Eleven of the twenty-one authors from the German edition are published in the selection presented here. These writers largely hail from Western Austria (Tyrol and Vorarlberg) and the South Tyrol, a largely German-speaking part of the historic county of Tyrol, now the province of *Alto Adige* in Northern Italy. Giants of Austrian contemporary literature, such as Friederike Mayröcker and Raoul Schrott, are represented in this collection as are aspiring young authors who are published here in English for the first time. It is noteworthy that many of these authors studied German and English/American literature at the university and are literary scholars and critics in their own right. Prose and poetry texts are balanced in the collection as well. The themes addressed illustrate the concerns of contemporary Austrian writing and the post-modern condition where reality is contested.

A number of people have contributed mightily to this project. Johann Holzner, a noted scholar of German and Austrian literature at the University of Innsbruck and a co-editor of this collection, contributed a new introduction to this English edition to make contemporary Austrian writing more accessible to those unfamiliar with it. Brigitte Scott and her students have done an extraordinary job in translating complex texts from German into English as have Richard Dove in his translation of Mayröcker and Iain Galbraith with Schrott's poems. We are most grateful to Inge Fink, a native of Vorarlberg and graduate of the University of Innsbruck's German and English Department and the University of New Orleans English Department, for her translation of Holzner's introduction. Inge has taught English at UNO for some 20 years now and has developed a rare feel for the subtleties of the English language. All of these translators have contributed enormously to make this publication possible. Birgit Holzner, the director of *i*up, Rektor Tilmann Märk and Matthias Schennach have inspired the publication of these texts in English, and we are grateful for their gentle pressure not to let this project slip. Bill Lavender, the director of UNO Press and a notable New Orleans poet himself, is never one to say no to the publication of poetry and inaccessible literary texts and was eager to help us finish the project. He has been ably assisted by Lauren Capone who did a wonderful job in designing the volume. At CenterAustria, office manager Gertraud Griessner, student worker Carmen Gächter, and research fellow Eva Maltschnig, have kept my back free to complete this book. It is the first in a new series of publications on "Studies in Central European History, Literature and Culture" to be jointly published by UNO and *i*up. We want to make Austrian and Central European historical scholarship, cultural studies, and literature more available to English-speaking audiences and are looking forward to many more titles being added to the new series.

Günter Bischof, New Orleans, September 2011

JOHANN HOLZNER AND ALOIS HOTSCHNIG

Introduction

translated by Inge Fink

The authors represented in this book have all been students or faculty at the University of Innsbruck, and many of them still work there. We collected these texts into an anthology so the university could stay in touch with its graduates, whose academic professions have scattered them across all academic fields, from arts and sciences to economics and politics, often in universities that compete with each other. We hope that the competition between these institutions will encourage the debate about the role of the university in society, especially in light of the ever-increasing skepticism concerning the value of what we are doing. Literature opens a window on realities that can shine a light on the fundamentals and possibilities of our world—often hidden to social and political administrators—because of literature's distance from everyday reality. We want to thank all the authors who have accepted our invitation to submit their work for this anthology.

Johann Holzner

Fighting for Survival:
On Contemporary Austrian Poetry

translated by Inge Fink

Many of the internationally known Austrian poets, especially those who experimented with language, have been dead for many years: Erich Fried, H. C. Artmann, Ernst Jandl, Andreas Okopenko, Reinhard Priessnitz. Unfortunately, few of the contemporary poets follow in their path, even though one can see connections between the work of Fried and Christoph W. Aigner, between Artmann and Raoul Schrott, between Priessnitz and Ferdinand Schmatz. Ingeborg Bachmann continues to be an icon, especially for young women writers.

It would be hasty, however, to assume that Austrian poetry is in decline, but its role has changed as a result of the social, political, intellectual, and historical developments in Central Europe after 1989-90. The old patterns of thinking and making sense of the world, familiar since the student movement, have lost their power. As a result, we have lost an organizational parameter that, while foregrounding political concerns, allowed us to create simple evaluative systems. The old system of thinking in black and white, of which we have always been suspicious, has become obsolete just like the so-called aesthetics of conviction, which have been off track since the debate about Christa Wolf, and, in Austria, since Robert Schindel's attacks on Fried's poetry and on any form of propaganda literature.

It thus comes as no surprise that contemporary Austrian poetry shows a tendency—possibly even more radical than before—to break open whatever still exists of former foundations and certainties and to keep both writers and readers in unstoppable motion.

The age-old distinction between artistic and moralistic concerns has long since become defunct and can no longer adequately describe the variety and peculiarities of contemporary poetry. If there is one thing that unites the works of contemporary Austrian poets, it is their skepticism concerning commonly held ideas about reality, about how the world is and how it could be, and their willingness to relativize these ideas without opening the door to arbitrariness.

The first poem to be introduced here comes from arguably the most important poetry collection in recent years, *Notes on a Camel* by Friederike Mayröcker:

Für E.J.

bei aufgeschlagenen Fenstern am Morgen eines leuchtenden
Augusttags solchem Augusttag / trinken
das Wehen der Luft / noch / sich sagen ich lebe / noch /
und jetzt und hier aber endlich
oder durch die blendende Bläue segelt die endliche
Schwalbe

For E.J.

With windows thrown open in the morning of a luminous
day in August such a day in August / drinking
the breeze of air / still / telling oneself I live / still /

and now and here but finally
or through the blinding blueness sails the transitory
swallow

Dedicated to Ernst Jandl, the poem's never-released tension between grammatical and poetic structure creates movement that can no longer find release in a calm ending. In addition, by choosing words with multiple meanings, Mayröcker problematizes the power of language to represent reality. From the very beginning, the poem yokes contradictory impressions as she talks about "windows thrown open"[1] rather than "open windows." It recalls the flirtatious batting of one's eyes, the opening of a book, but, at the same time, the violence implied in the word "to beat" evokes both affection and pain. It underscores both the evanescence and fullness of life—"still / telling oneself I live / still"—while the contrast between "transitory" and "infinite" intensifies the pain. As if contradiction were the most natural thing in the world, the swallow at the end indicates both happiness and unhappiness, the perception of all things fascinating, and the ancient realization that one swallow does not make a summer yet.[2]

---

1. Literally, the phrase "aufgeschlagen" means "beaten open;" while this represents an unusual use of the word in this context, German readers will still get the primary meaning of "wide-open" or "thrown open." Unfortunately, this meaning is not readily available in English. The association with "Augenaufschlag," the act of (coyly) raising one's eyes (to a lover), cannot be sustained in translation either.
2. The German idiom "eine Schwalbe macht noch keinen Sommer" means that a single swallow, although considered a harbinger of summer, alone is not enough to prove that summer has, indeed, come.

Far from tempering or even eliminating these kinds of contrasting observations, contemporary Austrian poets painstakingly register these in a variety of ways and integrate them into the texture of their poems. Salzburg-born C. W. Aigner (recipient of the 1996 Else Lasker Schüler Award, the 2003 Anton Wildgans Award, the 2004 Dresdner Stadtschreiber Award, and the 2006 Austrian Appreciation Award for Literature) has tried to explain this literary method. He says that the changes we observe in contemporary poetry stem from a shift in our perception of the responsibilities of literature. In the past, literature was dedicated to "information and enlightenment, indoctrination and seduction," but other disciplines have taken over this task, leaving the arts free to "explore in all directions as artists search for ways to represent their idea of the world and for the language that will express what they have found." Aigner's poems show this technique of exploration as he tries to chip away at the limitations of our perception.

Im Weinberg mit Skácel

Am dunkelblauen Faden
zwischen Jupiter und Venus
hängt der halbe Mond und tropft
in unsere Karaffe

Grillen. Bis zu den Schultern
stecken wir in ihrem Lärm
Er sagt: Die einzigen die an
den eigenen Beinen sägen

Wir trinken traurig aber wahr

In the Vineyard with Skácel

On a dark-blue thread
between Jupiter and Venus
hangs the half-moon and drips
into our carafe

Crickets. Up to our shoulders
stuck in their noise
He says: The only ones who
saw away at their own legs[3]

We drink sad but true

The poem comes from the collection *The Denial of the Pendulum Clock*. At first glance, it presents us with a snapshot of an encounter, written in simple words, as if the poet is trying to undercut any autobiographical narrative tone. Yet, once we look closer, the poem offers a comment on the role of poetry in a world that has grown cold, a world in which "noise" overrides and erases the magical, enchanting tranquility of the universe. No longer reversible (as indicated by the use of the present tense), this process of erasure determines the perception of beauty (the moon, the "half-moon," how different from the moon in Romantic poetry, "hangs" and "drips") and suggests the thought which is here attributed to Skácel ("The only ones who / saw away at their own legs"). In the end, the speaker is so depressed by the situation that he/she refuses to answer or

---

3. The line references the German idiom "am eigenen Ast sägen," which translates as "sawing away on the branch one is sitting on" and describes an action that will come back to hurt the person performing it.

even say a word. Or so it seems. His/her reaction lies in the poem's structure, which turns the simplest lexical elements ("thread," "crickets") into metaphors and shimmering phrases, which are anything but mute and apathetic. Not one of these sentences could be paraphrased or translated into everyday language; every word connotes two, three, or more meanings; every vowel contributes to the distance between deep mythical space and the level of crickets. As a result, the poem, sad but true, laments the way of the world at the same time as it names and illuminates what is and what it could be.

According to Aigner in his "Comments on the Term 'Art,'" art has always brought forth "objects of great charm and magic" that, through the millenia, have outlasted "all kinds of powers with their ideological or moral claims to exclusivity" and "still move us." As he sees it, art is misguided if it does no more than mingle with the noise of everyday life, a view shared by Skácel, Sarah Kirsch, and Reiner Kunze.

Far from tempering or even eliminating the kind of contrasts produced by everyday noise, contemporary poetry painstakingly registers perceptions as they tumble on top of each other and integrates them into the structure of the text. Similarly, the title of Michael Donhauser's "Silent Things" contrasts sharply with the rest of the poem:

Stilles

Gleisen, sanftes, ein Schlagen und
Landschaft, eine Wange als Hügel
Hügelzüge und Weiher, Zeilen, die

Felder bestellt, öd und spät mit
Herbstlichem, gelbem, dem Laub

Schauen, langes, und Weichen, ein
Wittern als Gezweig, als Bewuchs am
Gemäuer, ich und weiss, weiss nicht
lege mich mit einer Biegung und weit
gesäumt von Bäumen oder entlang

Schatten, ein Wanken, weiches und
Zittern, Flimmern, ein Nahbei als
Weile, blaues oder Wild mit Tritten
Spuren, gekrönt von Haufen, von
Blättern: dein stilles Gesicht

Wir streiften, ich zähle, Farben, das
Erröten, Tönen, orangen und hell als
Zurechtziehen, verfliegendes, Lächeln
wir wären, sagt es, und ein Weg
nennt oder gegangen den Sommer

Dass es und will oder Abend und
Gestänge, himmelwärts mit Vögeln wie
leiser und werden, während ein letztes
lose im Nussbaum und hängend, ein
Verlieren wie stündlich fast schlägt

Leuchtend, wir sassen, es lag und
weitheranflutend, lag Licht, war, ich
schlug, duftend und schlug es den
Herbst, höre, die Böschung, Sigrid, es
nahmen die Strassen uns und auf

Doch oder dann, scheinend und wird
dunkler es tiefer und milder das Wort
bricht, dass und Sprachen nur bleiben
Nächte, ich nannte, die Kälte, es
fiel: der silberne Schlaf

Silent Things

Glistening[4], softly, banging and
landscape, a cheek as a hill
rows of hills and ponds, rows, the
fields tilled, bleak and late with
autumn, yellow, the leaves

Looking, long, and yielding[5], a
sniffing the wind as branches, as a growth on
the wall, I and know, do not know
lie down with a bend and far
lined by trees or alongside

Shadows, a swaying, soft and
trembling, shimmering, a nearby as
a while, blue or deer with footprints
tracks, crowned by piles of
leaves: your silent face

---

4. The word "gleisend" (a present participle) does not exist in German;
there is no verb "gleisen." "Gleis" refers to (railroad) tracks, which could
evoke the meaning of "gliding" (as if on a rail). "Gleissend," on the other
hand, means "glistening," the meaning I chose here.
5. "Weichen" can mean two things in German: "railroad switches" (a
meaning that would correspond to the reference to tracks in the previous
stanza), but it also means "to yield" (here in its gerund form). I chose the
second meaning here.

We roamed, I'm counting, colors, the
blush, sound, orange and bright as
straightening up, fleeting, smile
we were, it says, and a path
named or walked the summer

That it and will or evening and
bars, heavenward with birds like
quieter and become, while a last
loose in the nut tree and hanging, a
defeat like hourly almost chimes

Radiant, we sat, it lay and
flooding from afar, light lay, was I
chimed, fragrant and it chimed
autumn, hear, the embankment, Sigrid,
the streets took us and in

But or then, seemingly and getting
darker deeper and milder the word
breaks, so that and languages only remain
nights, I named, the cold it
fell: silvery sleep

An avalanche of words, with never a period to separate
what we need to see together. Instead we have broken-down
syntax, recurring phrases and phonetic elements as loosely
connected thoughts, providing a glimpse of the speaker's
world, his past and his present, which would never have been
possible with a linear sequence of carefully finished stanzas.

As soon as one image emerges, it disappears and is overlaid by a new one, which often contradicts the first. As soon as the contours of a landscape become visible, we catch a glimpse of a relationship which simultaneously includes wanting to be alone and having to be alone, and emotions like love and pain. As soon as we get a glimpse of the past, the memory suddenly breaks off, flooded by associations that will let go of the speaker only after they have been crowded out by others. The regularity of the stanzas does not create a mirror to reflect calm and "silent things;" instead, it creates a film that enhances the tensions of things stretched to the breaking point or already breaking. The breakdown suggested in the text—in the way it draws boundaries and establishes multiple links— becomes the cipher of a consciousness that would be chaotic if the poem did not offer some kind of control through its artificial form.

Author Michael Donhauser, born in 1959 in Vaduz, received the Manuskripte Award in 1990, the first Christine Lavant Award for Poetry in 1995, the Meran Poetry Award in 2004, the Ernst Jandl Award in 2005, and the Georg Trakl Award in 2009. Coming from a different direction, Robert Schindel, born in 1944, recipient of the Ernst Fried Award, rejects, like Fried, all simple connections and the negative alliance between literature and politics. In his Vienna lectures, he defines literature pithily as "the information office of fear." What he means by this becomes clear in the first few stanzas of "Vineta I."

Vineta I

Ich bin ein Jud aus Wien, das ist die Stadt
Die heiße Herzen, meines auch, in ihrem Blinddarm hat
Die schönste Stadt der Welt direkt am Lethefluß
Ich leb in ihr, in der ich so viel lachen muß

Einst Welthauptstadt des Antisemitismus ist sie heute
Vergessenshauptstadt worden. In ihr lachen Leute
Die für das nackte Leben grad gnug Tränen haben
Sitzen in der Dunkelküche, eine halbe Welt geladen

Vineta I

I am a Jew from Vienna; that is the city
That has hot hearts, mine included, in its appendix
The world's most beautiful city right on the Lethe river
I live here, where I must laugh so much

The former capital of anti-Semitism, today she is
The capital of forgetting. People laugh here
Who have just enough tears for their naked lives
They sit in the dark kitchen, half a world loaded

The "information office of fear" does not just give out ambiguous information. Quite to the contrary: assuming that all he has to do is to imitate his creator's speech, the speaker uses very clear language when he finds it proper and necessary to speak plainly, as is already evident in the title, which refers back to Jura Soyfer. He is equally clear whenever he refers to the holocaust. By employing and mixing different stylistic levels, the speaker identifies himself as an observer of the scene who sees everything and who will conquer any opposition regardless of where it comes from.

However, the speaker gets so tangled in phonetic and syntactic webs, sometimes in individual words, that the most diverse strands of associations come together or drift apart from one rhyme or sentence to the next. As a result, the boundaries between beauty and darkness, laughing and crying, heat and cold dissolve, and words like "loaded" yoke together connotations in a Gordian knot that can never be untangled. What remains is uncertainty, even (or especially) when the speaker believes that he knows everything.

Vineta 2

In Wien kenn ich dir jeden Stein
Paul Stein am liebsten, jeden Stern
Am lachendsten den Willy, jeden Hochroizpointner Karli
Den Präsidenten aber auch den Ratzer Charlie

In Wien kenn ich die meisten der Kastanienbäume
Und jeden Mokka, ob beim Kalb oder im Prückel
Den Rotwein sowieso, den Heurigen der Brünnerstraße
Den Stephansdom um halb vier morgens fest im Augenmaße

Kenn dir den Wiener, ob vermummt als Trafikant
Oder herausgesagt vor allen Ohren als Sekkierer
Die Frauen kenn ich dir, ob aus Hernals
Oder verhuscht im Wiental allenfalls

Was ich nicht kenn in Wien, was kenn ich denn?
Den Radius der liederlichen Einöd Stufensteigen?

Vom Hörensagen kenne ich den echten Judenscherz
Und mit der Zahnbürste spür ich des echten Wiener Herz

In Wien kenn ich dir jeden Stein und jeden Stern
Lebe in dieser Stadt so mittelgern

Vineta 2

In Vienna I know every stone[6]
Paul Stein being my favorite, every star
Most laughingly Willy, every Karli
Hochroizpointner
The president, as well as Charlie Ratzer

In Vienna I know most of the chestnut trees
And every mocca, at Kalb's or Prückel's
Not to mention the red wine, the new wine[7] of Brünnerstraße
St. Stephen's cathedral at three-thirty in the morning, solidly
eyeballed

I know the Viennese, bundled up like a newsstand vendor
Or declared by all ears as a bully
I know the women, both from Hernals
Or timid in the Vienna valley as the case may be

What don't I know about Vienna, what do I know?
The radius of the slovenly desert climbing the steps?

6. "Stein" in German means "stone, rock," but here it refers to the person
Paul Stein; the same is true for "Stern" ("star").
7. "Heuriger" has two meanings: it refers to new ("this year's") wine but
also to a wine bar where customers can sample new, locally grown wine.
These "Heurigen" bars are a common sight in any wine-producing area in
Austria.

I know the real Jewish jokes from hearsay
And feel the real Vienna heart with the toothbrush

In Vienna I know every stone and every star
I like living here so-so

Judging by the use of spoken language, the poem first reveals the speaker as somebody who is very familiar with everything Austrian and Viennese. In addition, as becomes clear as we read on, a whole world is revealed, a world that is much more complex than the speaker suggests at first, a city in which the most innocuous things such as stones or stars can bring to mind the darkest chapters of Austrian history. Keeping things secret or hushing them up may work as long as the uninitiated listen to the self-appointed tour guide, but if the audience, to whom the speaker bares his soul, knows at least the basics of Viennese (cultural) history, secrecy turns into an act of communication.

Only the naive or the ignorant reader would assume that the "president" in Vienna must be the president of Austria or of the Austria Wien soccer club. Only someone completely uninformed would not be startled to hear that a Hochroizpointner lurks in every district in Vienna. The charming yet unfeeling Austrian tendency to nickname every Mr. Karl "Karli" cannot hide the fact that the grandsons of the legendary Hochroizpointner (who spelled his name with a "tz" in the days of Arthur Schnitzler) are the spitting image of their grandfather: hair slicked back, a small mustache, fencing scars —just the way Schnitzler, in his comedy *Professor Bernhardi*, painted the image of a "candidate," who has observed every department in the Elisabethinum, his place of work, and who boasts a store of "many patriotisms."

The speaker finally suspects that not all that glitters like the "real Viennese heart" is gold, that he himself might turn out not to be a real Viennese after all and might go down at any point.[8] It thus comes as no surprise that the conclusion he presents in the last line of the poem comes out differently than one would expect after his initial brisk speeches. "Fear is locked up in the word," Schindel states in his Viennese lectures; "dense, in a manner of speaking, it is thrown from a dark ground; it is dark itself, but the ground has become less dark." Needless to say, this kind of poetry is hardly apolitical.

But this poetry has a life of its own and is thus far removed from the kind of political poetry Erich Fried has so often defended and written. This life of its own, however, has its advantages and disadvantages.

On the one hand, this kind of poetry cannot be hitched to any cart, not the cart of power or the cart of the opposition. On the other hand, poetry like this is easily overlooked; it seems to fight for its life at the bottom of a wave.

And this is how it is: contemporary Austrian poetry must fight for its continued existence. It rarely makes the bestseller lists, unlike Artmann's *med ana schwoazzn dintn (With Black Ink)* or Fried's *Es ist was es ist (It Is What It Is)*. However, the Austrian literary landscape contains potentially innovative

8. The author here makes reference to a popular Austrian TV series, *Ein echter Wiener geht nicht unter*, which translates as "a real Viennese will not go down."

poems that combine aesthetic sophistication and emotional depth, such as Sepp Mall's poem *"Wechselnde Anschriften,"* which lends this anthology its title:

Wechselnde Anschriften I

Immer wieder ein Frühling
ein Grün
das ans Licht drängt
und kosende Paare unter Bäumen

Frag mich nicht / was
dauert: wechselnde An-
schriften / verblassende Bilder
manchmal ein Geruch
der sich mitten ins Er-
innern setzt
: von modrigen Haus-
aufgängen / kleinen Zimmern
wo du dich umdrehst
und sagst: wir bleiben

Changing Addresses[9]

Spring, time and time again
a green
thrusting up towards the light
and caressing couples under the trees

Don't ask me / what
will last: changing
addresses / fading images

---

9. The translation of the poem is taken from the translation submitted by Brigitte Scott.

sometimes a smell
that settles amidst re-
collections
: of moldy stair-
ways / small rooms
where you turn around
and say: here we stay

First published in the poetry collection *Landschaft mit Tieren unter Sträuchern hingeduckt* (Innsbruck, 1998), the poem evokes a scent worthy of remembering: "a smell / that settles amidst re- / collections." This is not a whiff of perfume but rather the smell "of moldy stair- / ways / small rooms," a scent of bygone days which still has the power to electrify the speaker, especially since it brings back moments that don't count for much otherwise.

But Sepp Mall is not talking about grand history; he is talking about love and spring and "a green / thrusting up towards the light." He counts on his trademark poetic language, deliberately simple, which resolutely eschews ornamentation but which conveys concise snapshots with stylistic economy.

Born in 1955 in Graun in Vinschgau (South Tyrol), the author grew up in an area in which, as he put it, "communication and conversation are largely restricted to essential things." This poem captures the essential things.

At least in the world made of words. In the *real world*, however, hardly anything that "will last" can be captured or discerned. Addresses change; images fade. The speaker is not concerned with the question of "what will last." It seems as if he is not only thinking of the Hölderlin quotation, "What remains, however, comes courtesy of the poets," but also of Erich Fried's laconic response in his poem "Lyrical Winter," "Was bleibt geht stiften"—"What remains escapes."[10] The speaker does not seek individual reassurance in the cycle of nature ("Spring, time and time again"); in this regard, he very much agrees with Fried. However, all of a sudden he changes his mind and starts to stutter (which is reflected in the structure of the poem) because there is "sometimes a smell / that settles amids re- / collections."

The poem does not capture the traditional scents of spring. The smell of "moldy" rooms intrudes upon the memory, not exactly a charming smell that anybody would associate with Spring. The speaker, who rejects the limitations of memory, is the only one who associates the experience of love with this odor.

The poem speaks of a bygone time. However, Sepp Mall's use of tenses does not indicate nostalgia or memory; he uses the present tense, which makes the poem not a conventional poem about the speaker's home but one of the most beautiful love poems in contemporary poetry.

---

10. The word play in this sentence is impossible to render in English. The verb "stiften" in German means "donate" or "endow." The idiom "stiften gehen" means "to escape" or "run away."

Brigitte Scott

Notes on Translation

Translating is always an exercise in approximation. While transferring the contents of the original text into the target language may be all that's necessary in some cases, even a simple commercial text forces us to consider additional aspects. How did the original text address its target audience—deferentially, casually, intellectually? Did its author adopt the voice of an expert? Is what sounds cool in German also cool in English?

The author of a literary text uses language very carefully. The translator thus must pay great attention to linguistic detail. When I was asked to translate the pieces in this anthology into English, I knew that I could and should not do this on my own. More than half of the texts were translated in a group project by the students of my translation course at the Institute of Translation and Interpreting. These students are Johannes Bartl, Vincenza Catalbiano, Coralin Farag, Miriam Gartner, Verena Gattermayr, Anna Kaminskaia, Roxanne Keiler, Stefanie Kuntner, Marina Lemme, Susanne Mader, Katharina Mantuano, Stefan Reinisch, Caterina Rigotti, Stephanie Toaba, Johanna Treider, and Katharina Walch. I tackled two additional texts by myself in the end. Luckily, I succeeded in persuading Scottish literature buff Andrew Milne-Skinner to do the final editing with me. Together we went through the drafts of the translations with a fine-tooth comb. During the debates about shades of meaning in German and English, about sound, rhythm and arcs of suspense, we became ever more aware of the decisions we had made more or less spontaneously. Translators do not necessarily think of theories or their personal take on literature; fine-tuning the texts in this anthology made us reflect on our individual positions and the linguistic choices we had made.

In the case of some poems, we asked the authors for feedback. These conversations showed how much writing and translating have in common. Both authors and translators are forever pondering how much they want to make explicit or how much they want to imply; they have to decide how much ambiguity they want to create.

Of course, translators cannot always achieve the author's agenda in the target language while retaining the same words and linguistic forms as in the original. Take, for example, the first stanza of Barbara Hundegger's poem "Family Album." The original reads like this:

ich über die stränge sie sich auf
keine seite er uns mit seiner eigenen
waffe ich aus der art ihr das herz
bis zum hals er mir das aus dem
kopf beide kein kapital aus mir sie
der wahrheit ins gesicht er mit der
faust auf den tisch auf mich ich
mir die nächte um die ohren taub

In a series of phrases, all of which leave out the verb "schlagen"—to hit, to beat—the poet recreates in linguistic form the typical characteristic of domestic violence: that it is hidden. Readers have to add the omitted word if they want to understand the poem.

Now there are plenty of English phrases with "kick," "beat," or "hit," but our initial attempts soon showed that such an approach would work for individual lines but would fail to yield a satisfactory overall solution. So then we took our cue from the title and tried putting together a family album with words, trying to recreate the way one might leaf through an album to show it to someone, pointing at various images: "that is me ice-skating," "here I was doing ..." and so on. In English, such phrases often start with "that is" or "here is." By linking all phrases elliptically with this introductory expression rather than the verb, we ended up with a much less clever solution than the German, but the overall form of the English version was now much closer to the original, giving us the freedom to stick more closely to the meaning of each individual phrase. The translation, which was approved by the author, reads as follows:

> me kicking over the traces her taking
> no sides him beating us with his own
> weapon me not true to type her with her
> heart in her mouth him putting it right
> out of my mind neither of them
> capitalizing on me her slapping truth
> in the face him thumping the table me
> me pulling an all-nighter numb

Let me give you another example; Kerstin Mayr produced a short prose text in which she deliberately used many words with double meanings, a great challenge for the translator. In this case, we occasionally compensated for the loss of ambiguity in one place by creating a double entendre in another, more suitable place. In Mayr's piece, two women are casually talking about a film they saw the day before. At the same time, one of them is rerunning a second film in her head—the memory of how much she once desired the other woman. As a result, she is only half listening to the current conversation and asks, "was?" This could, of course, be translated as "what?" or "what did you say?" in English, but the short form is fairly rude and the longer one too explicit. "Pardon?" would be another possibility, but that struck us as too formal. We ended up choosing "Come again?" which is casual enough and expresses her secret desire.

Elsewhere in the original, the author quotes an English song title: "What a difference a day makes." Had we kept this title in the English version, its effect would have been different. The students who worked on this translation solved the problem by using a French line that sounds like a quote, regardless of whether there is such a song or poem. In this way, they achieved a similar degree of deviation from the surrounding text.

Or take the short story by South Tyrolean author Birgit Unterholzner. In contemporary fiction, mood has become more and more important while plot and characterization have played a diminishing role. Birgit Unterholzner's story focuses on moods and atmosphere, which, in turn, tell us something about the characters. As translators, we tried to recreate the heat inside and around the main character and the charged atmosphere of the original by taking extra care in our choice of adjectives and verbs.

The title "Die Schnabelfrau" posed a major problem. In English, unlike German, it is not so easy to create a new word by putting together two existing words, here Schnabel and Frau (beak + woman). The students working on this text felt that Schnabelfrau reminded them of Schnabeltier (Engl. platypus or duckbill) and so came up with "The Duckbilled Woman." This sounds intriguing enough but has one major drawback— English distinguishes between "bill" for a round beak like that of a duck, and "beak" for a pointed beak. The beak in this story is definitely pointed and belongs to an Italian carnival mask. However, one cannot say "the beaked woman," and "the woman with the beak" sounds lame and seems to demand an adjective before "beak," such as "long beak," "sharp beak," or something similar. I became more and more convinced that the inclusion of the word Schnabel would inevitably distort the implications of the German title. I pointed out to the author that "beak" is a synecdoche, standing in for the mask, which completely hides the wearer's face and identity. So, with the author's approval, we changed the title for the English version into "The Woman with the Bird Mask."

Changing Addresses

CHRISTOPH W. BAUER

Gedichte

fremd bin ich eingezogen unter meine haut,
so lässt sich das am anschaulichsten sagen,
im spiegel das visavis, es bleibt unvertraut,
besser so als anders, kein grund, zu klagen,
das hirn vollgepumpt mit sehnsuchtsdrogen,
mit chimären, die den winter pulverisieren,
der blick hat sich den raum zurechtgebogen,
um die tür nicht aus den augen zu verlieren,
sitze ich in mir mit dem rücken zur wand,
tu so, als hätte es sich zwangsläufig ergeben,
die koffer griffbereit, den pass in der hand
wie ein schlafgänger im körpereigenen haus,
keine ahnung, was mich treibt, so zu leben,
ich weiß nur eins: fremd zieh ich wieder aus.

CHRISTOPH W. BAUER

Poems

a stranger I arrived under my skin
expressing it like this is most concise,
my image in the mirror, always unfamiliar,
I won't complain, it's better so than otherwise
the brain pumped full with drugs of yearning
with fancies, powders to defy the frost,
my gaze has bent the room to fit the mind
to keep a close watch on the door
I sit within myself, my back against the wall
behave as if it had to come to that
passport and luggage ready, all in all,
a paying guest inside my body's hut
not knowing what would make me live like that
I just know this: a stranger I depart

und wieder rasten die felder und kein gatter
hielt sie auf, sie rasten und rasten augenwärts
im säbelrasseln der kälte, geschliffene cutter,
die den tagen den weg abschnitten, ins herz,
in die lunge, in alle organe rasten die fluren
und froren ihn ein vom schnabel bis zum sterz,
den vogel, der im volksmund die glücksuhren
aufzog, er hing ausgependelt in seiner voliere
als wappentier zu wort gekommener lemuren

und deren tiraden aufs vermaledeite ephemere.
vom mythos einst gedrillt zu seelengangstern,
denen der tod das sprungbrett war zur karriere,
verkamen die manen zu nostalgiegespenstern,
konsequent allemal, waren doch die sommer
hier schon immer ein spuk. aus werbefenstern
voll affiger gebärden schaukelte ein frommer
wunsch sich auf die lippen und wurde mitesser
am täglich gereichten teller, hurtig klomm er

übern gaumen hinein in die bodenlosen fässer,
an denen sich land und herkunft leer kübelten,
und lief abgedroschenen metaphern ins messer,
war im wort und somit im eimer. dort dübelten

and the fields were on the move again with no gate
to stop them, they rushed and rushed towards the eyes
in the sabre-rattling cold, sharpened cutters,
cutting off the path of the days, into the heart,
into the lungs, the fields rushed into all the organs,
and froze it from beak to tail,
the bird that in common parlance wound up the clocks of
happiness, it hung limply in its aviary
the coat of arms of lemurs who had had their say

and their tirades about damned evanescence.
once trained by legends as soul gangsters,
with death as the stepping-stone of their career,
the spirits decayed into nostalgic ghosts,
consistent in a way, as the summers
here had always been a fantasy. from display windows
full of apish gestures a pious
wish slid onto the lips and became a parasite
on daily meals, climbing swiftly

across the palate into bottomless barrels,
from which land and origin filled themselves empty,
and walked into the trap of clichéd metaphors,
gave its word and so went down the drain. there, vowels

vokale die haken, an die das ohr sich hängte,
um zu überhören, was hinter der zergrübelten
stirn teutonenblechern durchs denken sprengte,
marschmusik, eine sprache stiefelnder natur,
die zum infarkt blies, die hirngefäße verengte

were putting up hooks on which to hang the ear
in order not to hear what, behind the deeply knit
brow, flitted through the mind in brassy Teutonic mode,
military marches, a language of boot-tramping,
which blew the signal for the heart attack, constricted the
      blood vessels of the brain

SABINE GRUBER

Leaves

When they drop they become a real pain for her; she bends down and shoves them into bags. Day after day I see her outside her door. Early in the morning, when I'm standing by the window with my coffee, she's already roaming her garden, crawling under the bushes and reaching for the leaves, leaves from the lime trees along the road and from the sycamores, which the wind has blown on her plot. She wears house frocks, blue and black sweat pants, her old anorak. Sometimes she's in such a hurry that, even though it's cold, she steps outside, scantily clad. I know her aprons made of small-patterned fabrics, the too short bibs and narrow tops, intended for another shape.

Her garden has changed; over the years the fruit trees have disappeared, pear and apple trees have been taken out, sewn up and stacked; she has replaced them with conifers that are impervious to autumn.

Each day she picks the plane leaves from the thujas, shakes the false cypresses, runs her hand over the nylon-covered garden furniture. She always starts from the right, walks along the hedge, turns around the garden shed and pauses on the street-side of her front garden, which is not much bigger than 100 square meters, without even looking at the traffic, at school kids or neighbors passing by.

A while ago, to save her back, she started using a skiing pole to spear the leaves with and pick them up.

She is the first one in the neighborhood to place bulbs in the earth, to drag the potted plants into the cellar. Her flower beds, too, are stripped. When, within a few days, the trees lose all their leaves during the early frosty nights, she stays out the whole day; she rakes relentlessly, rips the nasturtiums from the garage wall that backs on to her plot, climbs up on the fence to shake the branches of the trees over the street.

I have always left the leaves; they protect the earth from the freezing cold, shield the delicate plants when there is no snow. I have even sneaked into her garden in the middle of the night and taken one of her bags to cover my flower beds with the leaves she's collected.

Recently she bought herself a leaf vacuum; it's noisy like a lawn mower. The fact that the grass thins out and huge patches of it disappear in the suction tube, together with the rotten leaves, seems to pass her by or simply doesn't bother her. For some time now, all those patches of black earth that cover her lawn make it look as if it were a football field for children.

I've already reached the point where I completely forget about my coffee when I watch her. She has taken to leaving her garden boots at the bottom stair, crossing the slabs in her socks. She's probably concerned that her knitted slippers, in which she walks out to the mailbox when the weather is fine, might get wet.

It's been a few days now since the yellow or red patches have disappeared from her lawn. Even if she keeps her windows shut and can't hear when the wind blows through the lime trees, she knows exactly when she has to go out again. Her eye catches even the most hidden corner of her garden. Her curtains are always thrown wide open, so wide that it seems as if there were no curtains at all. Unlike me, she doesn't seem to mind the daylight, even during summer time. I prefer the semi-darkness to the glaring sun; it softens the edges and lines of my furniture.

A couple of weeks ago, I got up in the middle of the night to scatter a handful of leaves on her flower beds because I can't stand this obsessive tidiness anymore. The next morning, before I even had time to make myself a cup of coffee, the leaves had already been swept away. She must have collected them that very night or at the crack of dawn. One day I caught her climbing on her neighbor's garage roof to collect the leaves that had gotten stuck up there and stuff them into her shoulder bag. She would certainly have used the leaf vacuum on the roof if only stairs had led to it; but here she needed both hands to climb onto the fence and hoist herself up along the gutter. Sometimes I have dreams of leaves raining from the sky, hard oak leaves that rot down only slowly, dreams of lorries burying her garden under the municipal autumn waste, or dreams of aeroplanes dropping parcels full of leaves crashing and exploding all over her plot. How I'd like to see her then! But nothing happens, the wind never picks up, and the weather remains fine.

I don't enjoy my coffee anymore since she started avoiding the garden in the morning; life is so boring without her. I stand by the window. Nothing crosses my mind. Her gathering up the leaves makes for my happiness.

I miss her aprons, the small purple flowers and the yellow check patterns. She had a taste for unusual fabrics.
I should start sweeping in front of my own front door, but it is easier said than done. The broom has long become too weak for the work required by what's been accumulating in front of my house. I could go across and ask her to lend me the leaf vac. But I shy away from a face-to-face meeting; so far we've never spoken, so how could I possibly ask a favor of her?

She must have turned into a night worker; how else could you explain the vanishing of the leaves that I've been throwing in front of her door for days now? Even though I've also been walking her plot after the onset of night, we never run into each other. The light is always on in her bedroom, but I never see her, even though I can spot the wardrobe and the edges of the bed when I scurry past her window. Perhaps she tolerates my little games while secretly dreaming of revenge.

The number of bare patches in my garden is increasing. I'm actually surprised at how easy it is to remove the dense layers of leaves. The fresh leaves falling here and there upon the newly raked lawn are starting to bother me. I've begun to get used to the green patches. They cheer me up.

When I wake up in the morning, I walk from one window to the next to see if there are any new leaves. I've become so tired and tense from my disrupted nights that I can't remember whether it was really me who collected them. It is possible that she's repeatedly been sneaking into my garden in order to clean things up. She hasn't got much to do. The conifers take away her job, already the lime trees are almost bare and the leaves that I scatter in front of her door are easily removed.

I've acquired a pair of binoculars; it can't be the case that I don't catch sight of her anymore. For hours and hours I keep on watching. The coffee boils over; my computer screen switches to standby again and again. I type in my password several times a day, but nothing else.

She mustn't escape me, not a single one of her movements, not even her shadow. I am more and more often distracted by the bare patches in my garden; and night after night they increase in numbers.

I used to take an interest in details: the faint tips of the lime tree leaves, the similarity between plane and maple leaves, the hood-shaped leaf stalks enveloping the auxiliary buds, the spherical inflorescences which sprout along with the leaves in May. Now I stare at the green grass patches, compare their shape; I constantly have to remind myself that I bought the binoculars because of her. By now, I even own a stand so that I can observe her house and her garden without shaking or trembling.

It's as if she's withdrawing farther and farther inside the house; she even denies me a single glance at her washing. The lines are abandoned, folded up, the clothes-stand leans against the bathroom window. The eye-pieces have begun to hurt my sockets, and I would doubt her presence if it weren't for the lights in her rooms being switched on and off.

I've already cleared the leaves from half of my lawn and will soon get down to the flower beds. To spare my clothes, I've begun to wear the apron-dress left unused until now. I wear the fabric inside-out so that she doesn't recognize the patterns. She shall not find out more about me besides what she already knows. I assume she turns off the bedroom lamp that early so that she can watch me better in the dark.

These nocturnal rakings use up my last bit of strength. I've torn down part of the fence to make it easier for me to sweep my leaves onto her plot. As always, she makes them disappear. She doesn't fight back.

I've run out of coffee, but have no time to go and buy some more. The teeth of the rake are bent after I've used it to scrape the leaves off the driveway. I've climbed up onto the garage roof; at last it is grey again, without any yellow or red spots. The lawn is finely raked. Not a single patch covered. The layer of mulch, gone. The leaves of the bushes, trimmed.

I listen. There is creaking and rustling in the branches. I can barely stand the wait.

When they drop, they become a real pain for me; I bend down and shove them into bags. Day after day.

Barbara Hundegger

auf z.* von deinem balkon aus

(z. = zaha hadid, bergisel-sprungschanze innsbruck)

seit ich sie sehe sieht
etwas mich das sah ich
nur ein mal und es war
nicht da nur berge

aus diesem friedhof die
mich umzingeln flieg ich
rückwärtszeitlupe auf sie
zurück nimmst du meinen
sprung in dich und gönnst
mir diesen anblick deinen
arm dein bein deinen atem
ihren strengen hals entlang

schon bin ich einzige einer
initiative für das fällen von
bäumen schleifen von
häusern versetzung von
vierteln für den immer
noch nächtlicheren
nächtlichen blick auf sie

BARBARA HUNDEGGER

at z.* from your balcony

(z. = zaha hadid, bergisel ski jump innsbruck)

since i've been seeing her something
has been seeing me that i've seen
only once and it wasn't
there just mountains

up from this cemetery
that encircle me i fly
backward-slow-motion back
onto her you take my
jump into you and you grant
me this view your arm
your leg your breath
along her rigid neck

now i'm the only one
of an initiative to cut
down trees to raze
houses to move
districts for the
ever more nightly
night-time view of her

seit ich sie sehe findet
etwas mich nicht mehr
das sah mich mehrmals
und es war da nur berge

pendel.ausschlag.befund

als sammelten sich in mir
kontinente schlügen im kopf
die landkarten auf als finge
mein herz sich in ein netz aus
spuren gläsernen namen atlas
wie wagnis kompass ohne pol

als drehte sich mir der
schädel wartete das
auge welche kugel in
es fällt land wüste meer

mein herz in kreisen über
die länder und wünscht wo
es landet wärst wieder du kühl
beschäumt und neu wie ein
glas aus nur ersten schlucken

since i've been seeing her
something doesn't find me anymore
that saw me several times
and it was there just mountains

pendulum.deflection.result

as if continents were gathering
inside me were opening maps
in my head as if my heart
got tangled in a net of trails
crystalline names atlas like
venture compass without a pole

as if my head were
spinning the eye waiting
which globe would
fall into it land desert sea

my heart in circles across
the countries and wishes where
it was landing there would be you again coolly
foamed and new like a
glass of nothing but first sips

als müsste ich dich aus
sehnsuchtssucht holen die
nicht zu stillen ist dich in eine/
nähe schreiben die nomadisch
vor den gedanken her zieht nur
bewohnbar bleibt solange dort
anzukommen nicht droht

schickst mir zögerliche küsse auf
wild entschlossenen karten in das
wandelbare haus vor dem ich rauchend
grüble nicht weiß wie es betreten als
ob es eine angemessenheit
gäbe rechne ich alles dazu

aus deinem abstand der riechen
will in meinen wohin luftlinien brechen
hostiensturzflug unser bild anhalten
wer wir wären würden wir uns so
sehn kein berufen abdruck kein
handel gibt eine richtung vor

als wollte ich gebräuche vergessen
die blicke das gähnen den pünktlichen
anruf als dächte ich koffer überstürzt
die wege als erhetzte ich das ohne gruß
ohne grund kuss der dir gebührte in
eine nachrede kopfschütteln geruch
aus gerüchen herz aus film

as if i had to get you from
the desire-ire that
can't be appeased write you into
a closeness that nomadically
treks in front of the thoughts
only stays habitable as long as
arrival doesn't impend

sending me hesitant kisses on
hell-bent cards into the
convertible house in front of which
i ponder smoking not knowing how
to enter as if there were a propriety
i add in everything

from your distance that wants
to smell into mine whereto beelines break
altar-bread-swoop stopping our picture
who we were if we would see us
like that no appeal print no
deal provides a direction

as if i wanted to forget customs
the looks the yawn the call on time
as if i thought of suitcases precipitous
the paths as if i rushed no greeting
no reason kiss that was due to you in
a rumor head-shaking smell
of smells heart of movies

als wollte ich die schatten
nicht die meinen rucksack
füllen und liefe gegen brocken
hausen im genick als wüsste
sich wieder weder wie und
noch als versänken die lieben
im rauch um meinen tisch mein
bett meine faust der nie endet

als müsste ich dich abhalten vom
platz auf den bänken aus sätzen
den jahren geklapper die völle aus
wasser und brot mich stillt ein hunger
was nicht und nah ist und schürzt ein
durst den mund dauern im stehen und
rauchen im nichts nach offenen türen
letzte seiten deren text nicht endet
halbe betten die ränder ins all

als gelte es zu entziffern warten die
stifte gestreckt zwischen überschrift
unterton als starrte ich immer größeren
kleinheiten nach als wollte das herz die
zweite ausdehnung vor sich meine hand
dass ich die entdeckungen noch machte

als wolltest du halten wenn du
hältst als sei spät was uns zu

as if i didn't want the shadows
that fill my rucksack and
run against lumps
dwelling in my neck as if
knowing again neither how and
nor as if the beloved were drowning
in the smoke around my table my
bed my fist that never ends

as if i had to keep you away from the
position on the benches of sentences
the rattling years the fullness of
water and bread a hunger appeases me
what is not and near and purses a
thirst the lips lasting standing and
smoking in the nothingness towards open doors
last pages with text that doesn't end
half beds the edges into space

as if the challenge were to decipher the
pens are waiting racked between headline
undertone as if i were staring after ever
bigger trifles as if the heart wanted the
second growth my hand in front
that i would still make the discoveries

as if you wanted to hold when you
hold as if what was lying at our feet

füßen lag über uns das vertane
ausschütten einen regen aus
wäldern in jahreszeiten sicherheit
während ich und während ich küsse
lasse silberlinge edelsteine als müsste
ich schwören lachend was sein

als zweifelte mich mein stern schütter
an als gäbe es versäumen als müsste
ich wieder die regeln erproben im
dickicht der bibeln der betten als
fügte ich mich der unverbindlichkeit
ein aber wollte eine einsamkeit wagen

als müsste ich warnen vorm zerschellen
des herzens an der klippe meiner fragen
stein meiner neugier messer meiner
rastlosigkeit dich zu kennen nicht
meinen aber alles wissen von dir

als ob immer schamlosere
sehnsucht nach diskretion mich
befiele wortlosigkeit luftholen für
den abmachungslosen tag dass
es gibt was kein symbol hat schweigt
dass gehört wird was eine flüstert
gegen die richtung die uns brüllt

was late over us the wasted
pouring of a rain of
forests safety in seasons
while i and while i kiss
let silverlings gems as if i had to
swear laughing be something

as if my star doubted me sparsely
as if there were a missing as if i
had to test the rules again in the
thicket of bibles of beds as if
i adjusted to non-committal
but wanted to dare a loneliness

as if i had to warn of the bursting
of the heart at the cliff of my questions
stone of my curiosity knife of my
restlessness not thinking that I know you
but knowing everything about you

as if an ever more obscene
desire for discretion afflicted
me wordlessness gasping for
the day without arrangements that
there is what has no symbol remains silent
that you can hear what one of us whispers
against the direction that roars to us

als fülltest du dich mit verjährtem
gesagtem als tickten in deckung
die vorwürfe minen als fielen wir
uns gleich um den hals als
verschränkte ich endlos die arme

als entzündete ich die beweise entfesselte
spuren setzte die fährte neu dass doch sinn
das ergäbe heimlichen halt als sammelten
sich versiegelte fässer als dröhnten die
raupen stürzten die besen als schriee
ich zwischen einem berg aus dosen
und einem aus blütenstaub

als trügen die einsichten ausblicke sich
mir im dunkeln zu aufblitzen die nie eins
gewechselt hatten zwei wörter gleichen
geschlechts gestirne befallen dich
gründlich irrlichter kommen an was nun

as if you filled yourself with the obsolete
words as if the reproaches under cover
were ticking mines as if we immediately
flung our arms round our necks as if
i crossed my arms endlessly

as if i ignited the evidence unleashed
traces laid a new trail that after all it was
making sense secret support as if sealed
barrels gathered as if the caterpillars were
booming the brooms were tumbling as if i
were screaming between a heap of cans
and one of pollen

as if the insights were carrying outlooks
flashing in the dark that had never
exchanged one two words of the same
gender luminaries seize you
thoroughly ghost lights appear what next

familienalbum 1 & 2

1

ich über die stränge sie sich auf
keine seite er uns mit seiner eigenen
waffe ich aus der art ihr das herz
bis zum hals er mir das aus dem
kopf beide kein kapital aus mir sie
der wahrheit ins gesicht er mit der
faust auf den tisch auf mich ich
mir die nächte um die ohren taub

2

kinderreich mein königspaar schlägt
mich aus gürteln mit zeptern ich bin
ihre länderei ich bin ihre diener ihr hof
staat ihr galgenknoten erreicht nur mich
die königinmutterseelenallein
der königvaterfreudenlos
vom boden der sänfte ihrer male
schweigt sie mich blutend an von der
couch dem thron der flimmert wackelt
holt er nach meinem kindskopf aus

family album 1 & 2

1

me kicking over the traces her taking
no sides him beating us with his own
weapon me not true to type her with her
heart in her mouth him putting it right
out of my mind neither of them
capitalizing on me her slapping truth
in the face him thumping the table me
me pulling an all-nighter numb

2

rich in children my royal couple beats
me out of belts with scepters i am
their lands i am their servants their court
their gallows knot reaches only me
the queen-mum-all-alone
the king-father-joylessly
from the bottom of the litter of her marks
she keeps silent at me bleeding from the
couch the throne that is flickering wobbling
he strikes at my childish head

Ulrike Längle

The Sinking of the "Romanshorn"

When was the last time a ship sank on Lake Constance? A proper ship, not a sailing boat? Surely not within living memory. High time then something happened.

For as long as Flora could remember, she had always been very keen to take the ferry. The first time had been when she visited Mainau Island at the age of six. Once there, however, she had not been too impressed by the swathe of flowers or the banana trees, but more by the Siamese pot-bellied pigs at the zoo. The Siamese pot-bellied pigs even put the occasion of having taken the ferry for the very first time in the shade.

That's why her first conscious trip with the ferry was actually much later. Again, it had been the crossing from Meersburg to Mainau Island and again it had been a mild day in late summer. She had been sitting with a friend of hers on the afterdeck, watching the old and the pink new castle vanish slowly at the waterfront, being fed by a constant stream of accordion music from the loudspeaker. This time the dahlias had been more impressive than the pot-bellied pigs, but at the dahlia queen competition she must have misplaced her bet because she had not won a prize. In Meersburg there happened to be a wine festival at that time, and Flora had danced all night long with a busload of dashing dancers from North Rhine-Westphalia, who had for some reason got stuck in Meersburg.

Her most recent trip on this ferry had been last autumn, when she had shown all the beauty of Lake Constance to a visitor from Graz, including, of course, Mainau Island. This was when Flora also realized that the ship from Meersburg to Mainau wasn't a ferry at all, but really an ordinary ship. In her childhood, she had had no understanding of these subtle differences. Before their return from Mainau to Meersburg, they had had to wait a while and the visitor from Graz, who loved to give himself over to esoteric ideas, had embraced one of the big trees at the landing stage to recharge his batteries. During the crossing, Flora had been sitting alone in the ship's restaurant, drinking coffee because her friend had desperately needed to smoke a cigarette and so gone up on deck. Outside had been too cold and too windy for Flora. Instead, she had read an old issue of the magazine »Bodenseehefte« and felt bored.

Basically, the crossings on a proper ferry—the car ferry, from Meersburg to Constance—were much more interesting. When it was busy, a whiff of the big wide world would drift across the ship. Everything was much bigger than on the Meersburg-Mainau line and, of course, there were the cars and lorries, too. When Flora had paid for her ticket, she would stroll around the various decks, sit down to leeward, but when it was cold she would sit in the ship's restaurant. Rarely, far too rarely, were there high waves; the ferry mostly made its way calmly across the lake. Once, by coincidence, she ended up not having to pay: she had left her car, gone up to one of the decks, and had unintentionally avoided the ticket collector by going to the toilet, then returned to one of the decks to enjoy feeling the wind on her face, and suddenly they had arrived at Constance. Apart from this minor pecuniary gain, things had always taken their usual course. No loving couples in cars or locked together in the toilet, no skating on thin ice, not even affairs on the ferries.

However, on the 2nd of February, 1993, circumstances dramatically came to a head. From a visit in Zurich, Flora had gone by train to Romanshorn via Frauenfeld. At the railway station, the way across the rails had just been roped off with a cleverly fixed chain, which by means of a weight disappeared into a groove in the ground once the railway official released the clamp at one end.

Flora had joined the queue of passengers who wanted to board the ferry, the "Romanshorn," a vessel of the Swiss Federal Railways. Even while the cargo from Friedrichshafen was being unloaded, what caught Flora's eye was a lorry which jutted out at least one and a half meters beyond the afterdeck. The sun was about to set, the horizon behind Romanshorn was turning orange. Passing by at least eight lorries from the Netherlands, Italy, and Germany, which all seemed to be heavily laden and were leaving the ferry, Flora boarded the ship with a few other passengers. A new line of lorries arrived.

In the passenger cabin, she sat down at the table in the far right-hand corner, where she always used to sit. A silent passenger with a jumper and glasses usually took the seat next to her. He was always absorbed in reading the paper and possibly belonged to an intellectual circle, since he not only read the *Schwäbische Zeitung*, but the *Süddeutsche* and the *Frankfurter Allgemeine* as well, and he smoked, even though it was prohibited. However, nobody seemed to be put out by it, he was probably known and granted licence to do so.

Today, at one of the tables next to her, sat an extraordinarily cheerful group: a woman in a tiger top, with a long blonde mane, brought a magnum of champagne and handed out nut croissants to her companions and to passengers at the other seats. Apparently, there was something to celebrate, but Flora couldn't figure out what it was. Everybody had brought plastic cups and toasted a cheerful occasion, which to Flora would probably remain a secret forever.

Farther back, a group of Austrian cultural disseminators had gathered, and in passing Flora eavesdropped on them— there was a black-bearded museum director, a headmaster with a piercing look and two indolent cultural officials.

Then the ticket collector did his round, with the ticket machine and cash register around his shoulders, and started to collect the fares from the passengers. Flora got a pink ticket, the silent passenger had a season ticket and the gentleman who was by himself and who was sitting at the table next to her received a bright turquoise ticket with the imprint: "CIV Lake Constance and Rhine. Passenger and car ferry, 50% off (he had a so called 'Swiss half-fare season ticket'), Friedrichshafen to Romanshorn or return, DM 3.40. Valid for 1 day." Flora tried to figure out whether the separation of gender was reflected in the colors of the tickets, until she noticed that she had paid with Swiss francs and the gentleman with the turquoise ticket had paid with German marks. She studied the back of the *Süddeutsche,* which the silent passenger was just going through. She managed to decipher *"Dispute about official bigwigs," "European solution more urgently needed than ever"* underneath an advertisement for Siemens/Nixdorf, "*Mercury over the counter*" and "*Liver cells as test instrument.*" At the other tables people mostly read *Blick* magazine with a bold headline about the baby abuser from Zurich.

Flora's idle mind turned to the menu of the ship's restaurant that offered regional specialities such as "*Alpsteinhüetli*" for twelve francs or "*Hot dog with potato salad.*" However, this kind of brain food couldn't satisfy her hungry mind, so she made her way out into the open, passing the ticket collector who had just counted the heads of his cherished passengers and noticed that two of the passengers hadn't bought tickets. He went from one table to the next and was almost disappointed when two men from the table of the tiger lady with the champagne bottle responded by showing him their season tickets.

Outside, the moon was shining through the clouds. The orange shimmer behind Romanshorn had long vanished; only a dim light was shining through the darkness of the night. The opposite shore was not visible yet. Flora assumed they were just above the deepest point of Lake Constance. Ambling over the deck, Flora noticed something she had never spotted before; there were hatches mounted aloft containing the life jackets, closed by flaps that were fastened with three wing-screws each. How long would it take to open the flaps? As Flora looked down on the heavily laden lorries from the afterdeck, and listened to the reassuring sound of the diesel motors, she was caught by a sudden and strong gust of wind and was hurled against the wall of the ship.

She clung to a barrel that happened to be standing there. The setting had changed abruptly; the moon shone down fully from the sky, fleecy clouds shimmered with an orange-silver fringe and, in the distance, where the town of Constance must be, a torrent seemed to be descending, because a moon rainbow arched over the black waters. However, a whirlwind was approaching from the east, which, to Flora's amazement and immediate consternation, was multi-colored. At the same time, a waterspout could clearly be seen lifting out from the dark surface of the lake towards the whirlwind. It could only be a matter of minutes till the combined whirlwind and waterspout would strike the ill-fated ferry.

Horror-stricken, Flora clung to the barrel and glanced into the passenger cabin, but nobody seemed to have noticed anything yet. The glasses above the counter stuck in holders, which prevented them from sliding off even when the boat was rocking wildly. Only on the tables had some confusion arisen. The blonde woman in the tiger top followed with a bewildered gaze the magnum of champagne that was rolling across the floor, the culture officials ended up noticing their beers pouring over their immaculate suits. Only the silent passenger was sitting calmly in the corner reading the paper, apparently unmoved by events around him.

But now the spray started to seethe. The ferry was swaying to and fro, a roaring boom filled the air. All of a sudden, the ride continued calmly, but before Flora's eyes a tremendous black funnel opened up that seemed to reach to the very bottom of the lake. Its walls shimmered ebony black and glassy, but the ferry was careering towards the center of the maelstrom. Flora remembered reading a story by Edgar Allen Poe and let herself roll off the deck with the barrel.

When the ferry crossed the sides of the whirlwind and the waterspout, the lorries had been washed overboard and were now being sucked down the shiny surface of the funnel. At the very bottom of the abyss, there seemed to be a massif of sharp-toothed jagged rocks, because from time to time objects popped up from the abyss which were completely shredded and splintered: timber off a Finnish lorry that looked like matches with bristles, bananas that were already mashed out of their skin on the black water like yellow threads, bales of fabric that had dissolved into colorful rags.

The eerily dark gleaming whirlwind was filled with a dull boom and with majestic ease it spiraled down towards its destruction. Flora's barrel seemed to have a favorable shape in terms of its aqua-dynamic and aerodynamic design as it was moving downwards rather slowly. All of a sudden, the Romanshorn shot past her, Flora caught sight of the passengers' faces—white as a sheet—who were pressing themselves against the window panes, their eyes and mouths resembling those from a painting by Munch. Something went overboard and then the ferry disappeared into the deep. The Swiss flag on the stern was the last thing Flora saw.

On the smooth surface of the funnel, something was approaching her barrel which she reached for with one free hand; it was the silent passenger who had taken the jump and now was clinging to the barrel with her. Shortly afterwards, a black-bearded head emerged from the depths of the lake, followed first by a blonde mane like a chopped-off scalp and then by the glasses of the headmaster with the piercing look that more than likely would not be piercing anybody anymore.

There were also nut croissants, which strangely enough had remained intact.

Lake Constance contained neither piranhas nor sharks, but the rocks had done enough damage. At the same time, the roaring subsided, the speed was decreasing, and before Flora and the silent passenger had lost their last bit of strength, they found themselves back on the surface of the lake, amidst a circle of frothing foam that was getting calmer and being replaced by a gentle sway, which was lulling the wreckage of the ferry and the remains of the passengers, insofar as they could float, into a sleep of death. The moon was still shining through the orange-silver rimmed clouds, but the shores were no longer impenetrably black, rather, they were lit up by numerous spotlights which searched the lake and soon caught Flora, her barrel and the silent passenger in their beam.

Suddenly, a fanfare pervaded the air; a lifeboat was approaching and fished the only two survivors out of the lake that shortly before had been raging. They were welcomed by a reception committee as the leading actors of the "First Lake Constance Sinking Festival," which had been organized as a once-in-a-lifetime open air nature spectacle by the tourist associations of the countries bordering on the lake. A large audience attended at the lakeside, as Flora and the silent passenger received a gift voucher for a weekend together on Reichenau Island, with guaranteed organic-biological food from the island's market gardens.

wind

ihre hand zum abschied in der seinen
nicht fest, wie sonst, nicht nah
durch die tür, fort, in eine andere stadt
über die straße, vorbei an viel zu roten bänken
am fenster die augen, zwei tunnels

ein wind ihm ins haar, das schwarze,
wühlte darin, verlässt ihn am morgen
zerbrochen liegt das windspiel am sims
kühl umarmt, so behutsam sie
eine rastlose nacht lang

juni 2007

wind

her hand in his, bidding farewell
not firmly as usual, not close
through the door, away, to another town
across the street, past glaringly red benches
at the window the eyes, two tunnels

a wind in his hair, black hair,
ruffling it, leaving him in the morning
broken, the wind charm lies on the sill
in a cool embrace, so gently—she
for one restless night

june 2007

unter freiem himmel

im warmen liegen wir nicht mehr
zwischen uns das lampenlicht
in den ritzen alter mauern und baracken
nur der schein des feuers gestern
flackern, brennen unsere hände noch?

an die feuerstelle dicht gedrängt
eingepuppt in säcke
neben leeren flaschen liegen wir
und an uns sucht das licht
immer noch um sonst

märz 2007

under the open sky

in the warmth we lie no more
between us the lamplight
in the crannies of old walls and shacks
just the glow of yesterday's fire
do our hands still flicker and burn?

near the fireplace, close-pressed
stuffed into bags
next to empty bottles we lie
and the light
still scans us in vain

march 2007

Kopfkino

Und?

Eigenartig!

Wie?

Anders!

Und?

Nur ein Film!

Sie rieb die Hände.

Linkesbeinundrechtesbein.

Gestern war es wärmer.

Ich konzentrierte mich auf meine Zigarette, folgte den Formen und sagte:

Soso–und stellte sie mir gestern vor.

Ich fand kein Bild dafür.

So viele Bilder und dieses konnte ich nicht finden.

Irgendwo, auf dem Weg meiner Hand zwischen Popkorn, roten Sesseln und der ihren.

Da ich sie jetzt ansah, hatte sie fremde Münder und blaue Augen im Gesicht.

Die machten ihr Gesicht laut und Stahl.

Das Gestern lag ihr noch warm zwischen den Lippen und da hörte ich nicht

und wie sie schwieg und sagte wohl deshalb *Was?*

Er hieß Henry. Hieß er doch? Aber das fiel gar nicht auf.

Du hast blaue Augen, sagte ich, *obwohl sie grün sind.*

Cine Mental

So?

Weird!

How?

Different!

So?

Just a movie!

She rubbed her hands.

Leftlegandrightleg.

Yesterday it was warmer.

I focused on my cigarette, followed the shapes

and said:

I see–and I visualized her yesterday.

I didn't find an image.

So many images and this of all I couldn't find.

Somewhere, my hand on its way between popcorn, red

seats and hers.

Looking at her now, she had foreign mouths and blue eyes

in her face.

They rendered her face loud and steel.

Yesterday still resting warmly in between her lips and so

I didn't hear

and how she remained silent and that's probably why I said

    Come again?

His name was Henry, wasn't it? But actually it didn't matter.

Your eyes are blue, I said, *although they're green.*

Das Licht, sagte sie, *das ist das Licht.*
Bald wären ihre Augen wieder grün und meine klar.

Mit jedem Zug dachte ich sie und mich in das Dunkel dieses
  Saals zurück.

Er war wie eine Kerze, die ausbrennt, von innen, langsam.
Man muss sie gar nicht auspusten, das kommt ganz von selbst.
Gestern, als ich die Kerze löschte,
da waren ihre Augen schwarz.
Ich muss meine Lage ändern,
das war es doch, was sie gesagt hatte.
Nachts.
Und dann ist es dunkel geworden.
Ja, und bald schon kam der Schluss, sagte sie.
Meinte Henry, meinte den Film.

Gestern sie, heute das Gestern in meinen Armen, dachte ich.
What a difference a day makes.

Wo stehst du, fragte sie.
Um die Ecke, sagte ich und meinte es auch so.

Im Auto klammerte ich mich an das Lenkrad,
spürte ihren Blick.
Was ist mit dir?
Wenn ich jetzt laut schreie, hörst du mich dann,
dachte ich und sagte *nichts.*

The light, she said, *it's the light.*
Soon, her eyes would be green again and mine clear.

With each puff I imagined myself and her back into the dark
    of this auditorium.

He was like a candle, burning out from the inside, slowly.
You don't even have to blow it out; that happens anyway.
Yesterday, as I snuffed out the candle,
her eyes were black.
I've got to change my position,
wasn't that just what she had said?
At night.
And then it became dark.
Well, and soon it was over, she said.
Talking about Henry, meaning the movie.

Yesterday it was her, today it's the memories of yesterday in my
    arms, I thought.
Une journée–quelle différence …

Where exactly are you, she asked.
Round the bend, I said, meaning it literally.

In the car I was clutching the steering wheel,
could feel her looking at me.
What's wrong with you?
If I scream loudly now, will you hear me then?
I thought and said *nothing*.

Sie sah mich an.

Ganz unverwandt, da ein Mantelknopf mir vor die Füße fiel.

Zu lang gedreht?

Ja, im Kreis.

Wie im Karussell?

Das ist für Kinder.

Liebes,…

Da hörte ich im „-s" das Kind.

In ihrer Liebe, der blauäugigen, grünen.

Ich bin eine Kerze, dachte ich, während sie aus dem Auto stieg, und

ich habe einen Namen.

Aber das fiel gar nicht auf.

She looked at me.

Fixedly, as a coat button fell to my feet.

Been twisting for too long?

Yes, in circles.

Like a merry-go-round?

That's kids' stuff.

Oh my lovely…

The "-ly" I could hear was for a child.

In her love, her blue-eyed and green love.

I'm a candle, I thought while she was getting out of the car,
and

I do have a name.

But actually it didn't matter.

Claudia Paganini

Golden Mountains

Yesterday. It was night. I have tried to phone, but the line is dead. It is snowing outside. There is no light on in the house. The batteries are flat. As long as we are alone, the generator remains unused. Oil costs money. 2000 meters above sea level. An inn. The landlady and the children are sleeping. My hands are very warm from the tiled stove. You can hear the glowing pieces of wood crackling softly. Nothing else. Then the door opens. He is carrying a crate of wood. So wide it is difficult for him to get in with it. From the outside snow is blown into the living room. I am shivering with cold. His face is shining in the light of the candle. His eyes are flickering. A layer of snow has covered his tousled and matted hair. Threads of ice seem to make his beard even mightier. He puts the wood on the floor. The crate hits the floor with unexpected force. No sooner do the pieces come to rest than he kicks against them. Senseless rage. As if it were a scream without knowing whom he meant it for. The snow has just come off his clothes. It will melt.

You are awake, he says.

Staring at me. An animal. They are afraid of him. The farmers, the guests, even the mountain rescue service and me, too. But not Margit. She is always the same insignificant-looking shadow at his side. Light-hearted, as if she alone had not recognized his presence. I am looking into his eyes.

I do not answer. His face is ravaged. Maybe this is why I am so gripped by him. The unfathomable emptiness behind his power and his rage. An emptiness, boundless like the winter which surrounds us. A hell of snow and ice, a horizon, the ending of which you cannot make out, the beginnings go too far back for memory to be of any help.

Maybe it is a kind of love. Or maybe it is the same boredom which has led me into the mountains, a curiosity without any reason, which I cannot satisfy.

You are waiting.

He bends down, opens the tiled stove and pokes the fire. He might be laughing all the while.

You are stirring up the ashes, Margit would say. And he, *I know what I am doing.* I am waiting. He will kiss me, my temples. I am moving slightly in his arms. His face is steaming from the work. The sudden warmth has turned his skin red. The beard damp.

Before you came, he is whispering, *I wanted to do away with my life. I hate this hut so much. But I cannot free myself from it. As if it were a part of me.*

Later, he becomes calm, almost gentle. A boy, he seems to me, in a peculiar innocence that captivates me. And although we hardly touch, everything in me is filled with endless tenderness it seems. His skin is smooth. I think of Margit and that she must know about us. But it seems all the same to her, routine like the days passing one by one, like the men from the village who still desire her, despite the children, despite her fading youth and despite his irrepressible jealousy, the drunks whose path she blocks, not letting them out into the snow where their traces would gradually disappear, endless serene sleep, she pushes open a door beside the bar and allocates them a place for the night.

Later, all that is left is the crackling of the wood, I grow sad. Perhaps because of my guilt or because I recognize now that we are strangers to each other.

During the day the children play beside me, I imagine feeling his hips under the thin fabric of his oil-soaked shirt. His hands touching mine, pushing back the jacket, unintentionally and aimlessly. Moments in which I dare not think about my present. Sitting near the bar, I hear Margit's voice, and I start asking questions. Why is mankind incarcerated in total certainty, I say.

Let it be, she says.

We are lost without the radio set, he shouts at her, his temper rising, I can feel the fear soar in me, even though he does not stand in front of me and does not address me.

She, by contrast, is calm. Perhaps a hint of mockery in her voice. *You won't succeed.*

Christa is building a tower. The baby is walking, taking my hand. I don't care about you, I say to myself, I will be strong and I won't be broken by you, as strong as your wife. Maybe it is true. I am 25 years old, hardly younger than her, for just one moment I wanted to forget myself. But now, as this moment lingers and months have gone by. Months full of snow, of cold, to which I have become accustomed, of uncertainty which makes me addicted, as if there were no other stimulation than to love, not to love, to desire, not to desire and to detest.

After this winter, I have told Margit, *I will depart. Then you will be alone again.*

Now we are alone as well, she replied. She said it with her usual calm, a calm I believe I am choking on. The children sit on her lap. They stroke her hair. They seem close to their mother. They kiss her cheeks. Everything is taken for granted. This morning they have said goodbye. Christa puts her arms around her mother's neck. Michel crawls after her to the door, while he is waiting outside. The wind blows snow in waves around the house. Through the dense whiteness you can hardly see their silhouettes. Then they return once more.

My wife, he grumbles, *is going out with empty batteries.* The tension emanating from him is oppressive.

And much as I usually search for his closeness at every opportunity, I wouldn't like to ski down to the valley with him now. She, though, seems calm. Without a word, she hands me the avalanche transceiver. I go into the bar and change the batteries.

Anyway, you go too fast to be able to find me, she reckons, one hand on the door handle. But there is no sense of blame in her voice.

Now we are waiting. They wanted to be back from shopping shortly after lunch. She rarely accompanies him. *I need you,* he said the evening before, and she nodded. Now we are waiting. Dusk is falling, but there are still snow-clouds rolling by our windows. I am restless. The children tire me out. They start to miss their mother. Again and again I carry the boy from the warm living room into the kitchen, stare towards the cable lift for the supplies, if there might finally be any movement outside as a sign that the landlord and the landlady have loaded the gondola in the valley and sent it up ahead of them. But the ropes stand still, the snow on the reels pristine. Behind the mist I can divine the peaks of the *Golden Mountains.* Nothing else. *Sadnig,* I say quietly, as I would call a friend, *Bretterich, Ofenspitze.* The little girl repeats my words.

We don't go outside any more, she whispers. *Only yesterday.* Her voice eerie like her mother's. Every word decisive.

Tomorrow, you mean, I reply. *Only tomorrow we will go outside again,* I correct the child as if to break her power and with it the power that her father, her mother exercise over me. Then silence falls. Even the little boy is sitting quietly, leaning against the stove, and I already doubt that we are breathing. The fire is getting weaker. I don't care. In two hours, if the parents have not arrived, I will put the children to bed.

Today. It is night. I have tried to phone, but the line is dead. It is snowing outside. There is not any light in the whole house. The batteries are flat. If we are alone, the generator remains unused. Oil costs money. The children are asleep. My hands are warm from the tiled stove. You can hear the glowing pieces of wood crackling softly. Nothing else. Again and again I go to the door. The storm pushes me back into the corridor. I do not see any light coming from the valley. Merely a vague glow behind the clouds, as if there were stars. The traces from this morning have long been erased.

I return to the stove, lean my back against its hard heat; the blaze sends out a pain that penetrates me, but my hands are shaking as if I were freezing. *It's nothing but your addiction for adventure*, my mother raged. *Because you cannot bear normality. Instead of completing your studies, you are playing babysitter.* Months later, I can still hear her words. Not an evening has passed, when I would not have wanted to cry, when my mind would not have shouted at me; away, just to get away from this inn, back into the valley, where everything is simple and pleasant. How many nights when I closed my eyes and could think of nothing but that it was a nightmare in which I was living and from which I could not wake. And yet. The mountain holds me, the *Großfragant* in its coldness and brutality, even though the landlady nods to me and smiles. *Just go if you want to,* on the very first day. *You would be the first one to last the winter.* She, the farmers told me, grew up here, overtakes the men with a pannier on her back. She is a blessing for the house, the old people bawl when they are drunk. *A strong woman, otherwise the alp will go to ruin.*

Suddenly I jump up. A whirr, I say to myself, behind the house, at the cable car. Hurriedly, I slip into my boots, snatch my coat from the peg, push open the door. I want to run, but the wind takes my breath away. Nothing but a dry cough, I put my hands in front of my face, lower my head, anything to defeat the tightness in my chest. Slowly, I move forward. Snowflakes land on my lashes, are whipped away and drift on. With every step I crash through the snow. And yet the path has been cleared. The wetness has already reached my waist, the cable car still seems beyond my reach. To protect myself from the rage of the wind, I sink to my knees, finally I gain some ground, get closer to the hut. *Go ahead*, it is roaring inside me, his words, although they date back months. *I'm busy.* My hesitation escapes him. *I could help*, I reply tentatively. *So we leave together later.* He pauses, time passes by, then he looks at me. It's the first time, since we met at the station, that I see his eyes. They are restless and seem to be searching for something. *I will catch up with you*, he barks back. Then he carries on with his work. I wait. *Loading gas bottles is no work for a missy like you*, he grumbles. *Off you go, I don't need you.*

The snow is sparkling in the midday sun. Early December. A cloudless sky. There is a shivering inside me. I see the cable car start to move. Behind the rotten wood, I discover a piece of my backpack, the crate getting smaller and smaller, the man at the wheel is staring somewhere into the whiteness, with his right hand he seems to control the speed. *I don't know the way,*

I protest once again. My voice is thin. I want to turn and go back, although that would mean conceding that my mother was right.

Now he laughs. In the rigid cold his voice seems to make the air quiver as if the crystals around us would have to burst, his scorn roars. *Up,* he answers. At last I turn away, follow the tracks up the mountain.

I have reached the hut. In its lee it is easy to breathe. With my flat hands I push open the old wood so that there is a little gap. Although the surface is rough and dry from the cold, the palms of my hands remain without feeling, for too long they have felt their way forward through the snow. As I reach the interior of the hut, I pause, lean against the wall. Through my jacket I can feel the pump, with which he pushes the oil from the cable-cart through to the cellar. I cannot hear the whirr. Only the wind, which seems to sing a lullaby in its waves. Carefully I face the ropes. It is dark. Down towards the valley the horizon is turning white. The reels are still, no movement, the snow is weighing down the ropes. Sometimes, one single flake unbalances the structure, unexpectedly a part breaks away, casually and of no importance. Only now can I feel the coldness. My wet jeans stick to my thighs, and although I know I have to return to the hut, I am gripped by a great tiredness and my limbs are getting heavy.

Look, an avalanche, the little girl smiles at me, then is disappointed because I only turn my head around slowly in the direction of the *Bretterich*, in the afternoon, as the tension inside me is growing, on account of the time passed, on account of the dusk, because there still is no movement from the valley. *Now you have missed it. Never mind,* I answer quietly, startled as the child suddenly grabs my arm.

Pay attention, over there, she barks at me. I follow her gesture mutely, the slope is still and rigid, a white blanket, forgotten and heavy.

You must be mistaken, I reply.

Listlessly, I arrange the toys. Then, suddenly, the room is rocked by a tremor. A roar, rushing into our ears with such a force that my heart starts to beat furiously. For a few seconds then, there is silence. The girl has run to the window, her brother follows her on his knees. I go towards them and take the child on my lap. Christa's eyes are staring at the mountain. She's been right after all, but she does not seem to care. Where there was snow before, now brown earth is shimmering through. Spontaneous avalanche, I keep thinking, a vast, a really vast area, I do not want to think any further.

It is night. I put my wet clothes above the stove. Warm steam fills the room. It is late and I should sleep. Once again I wander through the dark living room, take the radio set and change the settings to grab any small chance of catching a signal, of communicating after all. I tighten the blanket over my shoulders. I am cold, although the damp heat, which is spreading from the tiles, has become almost unbearable.

In a few hours the children will wake up, wanting their mother. What will I say then, I consider, but without hope of really knowing. We are cut off from the valley, I think, with both kids it is impossible to leave. The mountain rescue service is the next thing that flashes through my mind. From the stove I scoop up a little water. Lukewarm, nevertheless, I drink. My eyes are burning. Nobody will search for us, I say to myself, if the innkeepers have not reached the village. Suddenly, the door opens. It is the landlady. She nods to me. She wipes the snow off her face. Behind her, a man from the mountain rescue service. As she takes her jacket off and strips off her gloves, she appears even more inconspicuous than usual, weak. Her face is pale, her lids swollen.

Is there some schnapps, the man shouts across to me.

Then he talks. About the avalanche. On the winter path, where no avalanche had fallen for ten years. That both were buried, but Margit had been able to free herself, digging out the man.

We did not want her to leave, but she put the skins on the skis, as if she had not noticed any of us. Then I just came along, he concludes, quietly and without great conviction.

Without a word, he drinks the schnapps.

Margit has come back from the kitchen. She eats. *You will stay here today*, she says to him and to me, *there has never been a night in which I was separated from my kids.*

She goes to the bar, the man follows her, pushes a door open, he does not dare to contradict her. Then, she turns to me.

How is he, I ask cautiously.

You should leave, she answers, *straight away tomorrow morning, he needs you more than we do.* And after some time, as I don't answer, *pack your things, then you can leave at sunrise.*

I nod slowly, I struggle to find the way to the stairs. Not until I am in my room do I start to really think. Hastily, I fill my backpack, get into my bed in my clothes. Even under the blankets, even in my sleep, the coldness penetrates me further. A burning ache that does not seem to cease.

Before sunrise I am awake already. Swiftly, I fold the blankets, I creep down the stairs. The door opens easily. No wind leans against it with force. Everything silent. On the peaks a gentle sparkle hints at the sunrays which are breaking through, and still with the first turn that I cut abruptly into the soft fresh snow under the cableway, my face is insensitive to the frost, the happiness in me uncontrollable, I already want to forget the night, to call nature a miracle, to love the *Golden Mountains.* So big is my longing for him, and lastly of the valley, that I let the snow carry me on and on, I scarcely notice the avalanche toe, which buried two men under it yesterday. Even later, when I have entered the *Stiegel Bauer,* drunk some warm milk and reached the hospital in his car, I reckon everything around me is easy. Forgotten the closeness of the snow, the constricting force of the *Großfragant,* my addiction. Only love remains, I think. He needs you more than we do. With her words I wave to the farmer, ignoring his silent eyes. With her words I run along the corridors, reach the department, call his name.

Who are you looking for, the nurse asks.

Josef Bacher, I answer, breathlessly, expecting to see him soon, to enfold him in my arms, to have regained my confidence in the valley to hold him tight and to say; You can free yourself, from the alp, from the inn, if you hate the mountain, you must not return now.

Josef Bacher, the woman repeats. A strange hesitation emanates from her.

Friederike Mayröcker

Traum Linien

damals bei blutüberströmtem Himmel ins Meer hinein *stapfend*, langsam schaufelnd ins stille Wasser während die Tränen mir über die Wangen, dachte : diese Momente in eine ewige Zeit eingegangen und würde es nie vergessen, dieser stöhnende Abend dieses funkelnde mein Herz zerreiszende Meer, also immer weiter hinaus stapfend, und langsam, nicht einhaltend zu waten, in den Schimmer dessen (nämlich einer Madonna), nämlich *der Silber Schwur*-eines Himmels der in den Horizont verschmilzt, während eine Barke. Aber er stand am Ufer und blickte mir nach mit einer liebevollen Angst ich könnte zu weit hinaus WÜRGEN, rief mich zurück, aber Himmel und Erde *blutüberströmt*, ich beobachtete ihn und die anderen Freunde, aber kein Wort aus meiner Kehle, Nachbilder der Sonne vor meinen Augen, und mein Herz *blutüberströmt*, ein Schauer von Blut usw., während die Kriechlöcher der Würmer, während die Höhlen der Würmer, während das Ornament der Würmer über dem Wasser, während die wehenden Wip fel (*diese Bürde*) am Strand, während ein Fink in der gekräuselten Laube, während das Votivbild der Ulmen, Tamarisken, Luzernen, während die Meeresströmungen.

FRIEDERIKE MAYRÖCKER

translated by Richard Dove

Dream Lines

back then with the sky bathed in blood *trudging* into the ocean, shovelling slowly into the tranquil water while tears across my cheeks, thought : these moments passing into sempiternal time and would never forget it, this moaning evening this sparkling ocean tearing apart my heart, and so ever further out I trudged, and slowly, not ceasing to wade, into the shimmer of that expanse (i.e. of a Madonna), i.e. the *silvery oath* of a sky melting into the horizon, while a skiff. But he stood on the shore and gazed after me with loving anxiety that I could GAG too far out, called me back, but sky and earth *bathed in blood*, I watched him and my other friends, but no word from my throat, after-images of the sun haunting my eyes, and my heart *bathed in blood*, a frisson of blood etc., while the bolt-holes of the worms, while the caverns of the worms, while the ornament of the worms above the water, while the wafting tree-tops (*this burden*) on the shore, while a finch in the rippling bower, while the ex-voto of the elms, tamarisks, alfalfas, while the sea's tides.

Der Holzboden im Haus : eine abstrakte Idee, eine
abstrakte Frottage, und deine Hand spiegelte deinen Kopf
: dein Kopf spiegelte sich in deiner zeichnenden Hand
(Max Ernst usw.), während du pflücktest das Abendrot der
horizontalen Farben, während die gegenüberliegende weisze
weinende Küste—Sakramente von Würmern, Exkremente
von Würmern im Meer, Prinzip der *Vielleichtheiten* in feurigen
Augen, mit feurigen Wangen, auf Knien du, Frottage des
Bretterbodens im Haus wo nur die nötigsten Requisiten, sagst
du, Schrank und Tisch und Bett und Stuhl, Matte und Herd,
Stroh und Holzkreuz und Zeichenbuch, Brot, Messer und
Meeresschwalbe (Zweiglein einer Glossographie usw.), *diese
Natur Passion*, Abdrucke der Profilsohle im Sand, kniend du
am Strand des Wattenmeers, in Zeitlupe, finde Holzkeil im
Sand finde Frottage im Sand finde Blut Sphäre die Himmel
und Erde hüllt und schleiert, finde rotblonde Haare mit
schwarzer Schleife, am Ufer kauernd, mit hochgebundenem
Schopf, orangefarbenem Bustier und Lendentuch, während
orangefarbene Handschuhe ins Wasser tauchend, der
Knochen eines Rindes, vielleicht Holzscheit, vielleicht Lauf
eines Hasen mit schwarzer Pfote, seitlich das Weidegras, dann
martert mir diese Rose als Spinnennetz über die linke Wange,
und in die Tiefe gestürzt, und Vogel Orgel weil uns die Kunst
erlöst, usw.

The wooden floor in the house : an abstract idea, an abstract frottage, and your hand reflected your head : your head reflected itself in your sketching hand (Max Ernst etc.), while you plucked the sundown red of the horizontal colors, while the white crying coast opposite—sacraments of worms, excrements of worms in the ocean, principle of *perhapsnesses*, in fiery eyes, with fiery cheeks, on knees you, frottage of the boarded floor in the house where only the most necessary requisites, you say, cupboard and table and bed and chair, mat and cooker, straw and wooden cross and sketchbook, bread, knife and tern (twiglet of a glossography etc.), this *passion for nature,* imprints of that rubber sole in the sand, you kneeling on the shore of the Watten sea, in slow motion, I find wooden wedge in the sand find frottage in the sand find blood-sphere which envelops and veils sky and earth, find red-blond strands of hair with black ribbon, squatting on the shore, with a shock of bound-up hair, orange-colored brassière and loin-cloth, while orange-colored gloves get dipped in the water, some cattle bones, perhaps log, perhaps leg of a hare with black paw, laterally the pasture grass, then I'm *wracked* by this rose as a spider's web across my left cheek and plunged into the depths, and bird-organ because art redeems us, etc.

Schlaf wie das Licht von Blumen in den Krügen, und durch das Fenster sehe ich wie du den Kopf beugst, dich auf die Knie niederläszt, so dasz man die Sohlen deiner Schuhe, ich meine gibt es ein Buch in deinem Schrank, gibt es einen Artaud, ach die Befeuerung deines Geistes im Anblick des Wattenmeers, vielleicht eine Glaubenssache, Weltschleuder, Seligkeit (Felsabgrund und unten das Meer, mein Vater mit einem Schuh in der Hand und unter Tränen), *die horizontalen Extreme*, sagst du, beginne zu monologisieren, wir sind umnachtet, die Badende von Picasso, sagst du, der Geist des Wassers

für Ulla Diedrichsen, 4. 5. 07

Sleep like the light of flowers in the jugs, and through the window I see the way you incline your head, sink to your knees, so that the soles of your shoes are, I mean is there a book on your shelf, is there some Artaud, ah the way your imagination is fired by the sight of the Watten sea, perhaps an article of faith, sling not for stones but for worlds, blissfulness (beetling cliff and down there the ocean, my father with one shoe in his hand and drugged with tears), *the horizontal extremes*, you say, I start to monologuize, we are benighted, the Bathers by Picasso, you say, the water's spirit

for Ulla Diedrichsen, 4. 5. 07

RAOUL SCHROTT

Physikalische Optik I

er kam aus dem november • der hagel brachte
    ihn herab • all das wasser auf den flügeln
die nähte und die grate einer gußform

    die im regen hing bis der wind sie kappte
und er dann an die scheibe schlug wie ein bügel
    der aus seinem schloß schnappt • der ahorn

dort und seine äste • so schwarz war er
    eisengrau der bauch • nur ein paar federn
zum schwanz hin heller doch kaum scheinbarer

    als seine schwere nun plötzlich am balkon
in die sich die krallen hakten • norwegen
    oder die tundra • kein anderes land dachte

ich mir ließ diese tarnung zu und dem schnabel
    nach zu schließen war es wohl ein sperling
augen dunkel wie mangan und ein ring

    ganz weiß und schmal fast wie abgeschabt
von diesem schauen • flüsse im winter wegwärts
    ein erzeinschluß in den pupillen • das herz

Raoul Schrott

poems translated by Ian Galbraith

Physical Optics I

it came out of november · the hail brought
    it down · all that water on the wings
the seams and fins of a cast

    that hung in the rain till cut by the wind
it struck against the pane like a shackle
    snapped from a lock · that maple

there and its branches · it was that black
    its breast iron gray · a few feathers brighter
towards the tail though hardly more apparent

    on the balcony now than this sudden gravity
its claws still clung to · norway
    or the tundra · no other land i thought

could warrant this disguise and judging
    by the beak it had to be a sparrow
eyes dark as manganese and a ring

    pure white and small as if scraped thin
by all that looking · rivers in winter along the way
    inclusions of ore in the pupils · its heart

ein flacher kiesel unter hagelschlossen
    zurückgelegt in den oktober • aufgehoben
war er leicht und das wort »vogel« eine vokabel

unklarer herkunft und von irgendwo im norden

    innsbruck, 22. 10. 96

a flat pebble among the hailstones
    handed back to october · picked up it felt
light and »bird« a word of obscure

origin and from somewhere in the north

   innsbruck, 22. 10. 96

Eine Geschichte der Schrift II

die nußfeigen des aviavy sind bitter auf den ersten biß
und süß erst am schluß • am hügel hinter dem schloß
trocknet das blut der hähne aus dem geronnenen blau
in das violett des abendhimmels • ein tiefer riß
bis zu einem weißen ring • im hof hört der pfau
nicht auf mit der zunge auf seinen steinernen amboß
zu schlagen • schreie die sich von seinem zwinger
aus weit unter die bäume bohren • zwei riefen
die über den geschwollenen fels laufen • einen finger
breit die in den roten granit gescharrten glyphen:
anus und vagina • sieben mal mußte man einen kiesel
in diese kehlungen werfen um zu kindern zu kommen
ein zum stein gesprochenes gebet das vom geniesel
des regens wieder den hang hinunter in das meergrau
des laubs gewaschen wurde • zu nutz und frommen
kaute man an den kernen und rieb sich den saft
auf den bauch • der tiere und der engel herrschaft
war an die früchte gebunden die im dunkeln glommen

ambohimanga, 4. 12. 96

A History of Writing II

the nut-like figs of the aviavy are bitter at the first bite
and sweet not till the last • on the hill behind the fort
the roosters' blood dries from the clotted blue
to the violet of an evening sky • a deep slit
to a band of white • the peacock in the court
will not stop beating its tongue on its anvil
of stone • screams from its coop corkscrew
downwards far beneath the trees • two grooves running
across the bulging rock • scratched out
glyphs the breadth of a finger in red granite:
anus and vagina • seven times you had to throw a pebble
into those flutes to get in the family way
a prayer uttered in stone and washed by the drizzle
back down the slope into the sea-gray
of the canopy below • to rub its juice on your belly
and chew the stones was thought of bountiful
avail • the lordships of angel and animal
they were tied to fruits that gleamed in the night

ambohimanga, 4. 12. 96

Graukogel

das kar • windholz auf dem jährigen schnee dürr und
zerstückelt • borstgras • in der leere die einem einsturz
vorausgeht raffen die wolken das gebirge zusammen
und die sonne zeichnet die schatten um in die fallinien
der nacht • jeder schritt weiter auf diesen tafeln zielt
auf eine mitte • aber das auge täuscht sich über fernen
abstand und höhe • was in der faltung des horizonts
sichtbar wird ist tage unbestimmt weit weg • das fenster
der tauern • heller hin zum rand des lichts geht die staffel
des massivs auf ins grau gestreuter bänder • glimmernde
linsen überschoben und dann verworfen und blenden
in einem kambrium von grüngestein • die tiefe die darin
langsam eindrang und erstarrte • relikte eines inselbogens
und ein flaches meer das nach und nach austrocknete
zum schelf und salz aus den rauhwacken löst • kristalline
formen bis in die achtecke des fossilen planktons und
das leben das sich auf den flächen festsetzt • ein kühler
wind fällt von der kante auf die gletscherzunge nieder
das skelett eines gebirges aus dessen fleisch die knochen
treten in einem geäderwerk von bächen • haut und
bauch • aber das hieße schon vom mensch zu sprechen:

Graukogel

the corrie • windthrown branches on the year-old snow
dry and dismembered • matweed • in the void
that precedes a collapse the clouds gather the mountains
together and the sun redrafts the shadows to fall-lines
for the night • each new pace on these slabs points
to an apex • but distances gradation and height deceive
the eye • what appears in the fold of the far horizon
is indeterminate days away • the tauern window • paler
towards its margin of light the step of the massif
merges with the gray of scattered bands • glimmering
lenses overthrust and then deformed and glances
in a cambria of green-stone • depth that slowly intruded
and set • remains of an island arc and a shallow
ocean that gradually evaporated to a shelf dissolving
salt from the rauchwacke • crystalline shapes
down to the octagons of the fossilized plankton and
the life-forms settling on their surface • a cool wind drops
from the cliff onto the snout of the glacier • the skeleton
of a mountain from whose flesh the bones protrude
in the venous workings of rivulets • skin and abdomen
but that would be to speak of man: nature does not know

die natur kennt keine schrift • spalten und risse lassen
bloß blindes am fels entziffern • erratisch grobe blöcke
und ein findling klafterweit von dem geröll einer moräne
weit oben an einem überhang reißt die kälte ihren keil
schroff in eine wand und die ausgesetzte spitze gleitet
ab viel zu langsam und unendlich stumm als könnte sich die
schöpfung mit einem mal in der verzögerung vollenden

habachtal, 13. 2. 98

of script • crevices and fissures allow us to decipher
only the blankness of the rock • erratically uneven
blocks and one boulder fathoms away from the rubble
of the moraine • high up in an overhang the cold gouges
its blunt wedge into the face and the jutting pinnacle
slides much too slowly and endlessly mute as if
creation could complete itself at last by this delay

habachtal, 13. 2. 98

Dämmerungserscheinungen II

der marmor der wolken • und dein kopf
aus dem dunkel gehauen mit schmalen
strengen gesten • die strähnen gerafft im
nacken die augen wie der schatten von
eukalyptusblättern die auf den stuhl
dort an der mauer fallen und die stirn
hell unter beiden händen • auf den fliesen
der terrasse hält die nacht still wie ein
insekt im spreiz der beine die zitternden
fühler aufgerichtet • vier fingerspann
über dem horizont liegt ein segment der
dämmerung • der bogen eines flügels der
sich schwarzblau mit dem wind schließt
und öffnet wieder • erdlicht • und nichts
mehr nun das sich berühren ließe • deine
lippen straff der geruch von kaltem holz
und die stille in der du dein hemd auf die
linke schulter ziehst • der morgen ist
etwas das über die hügelkuppe kommt
weit und unaufhörlich in indischem
rot • wir aßen orangen im dunkeln

vathi, 24. 8. 97

Twilight Phenomena II

the marble slabs of the clouds • and your head
hewn from the dark with gestures lean and hard •
the strands of hair gathered on your neck eyes like
the shadows of eucalyptus leaves that fall on the
chair by the wall and your brow bright beneath
both hands • on the tiles of the terrace the night
stands as still as an insect its legs apart raised
antennae trembling • at four fingers breadth above
the horizon lies a segment of the dawn • the curve
of a wing closing bluish-black on the wind and
spreading again • earthlight • and nothing now that
could be touched • your lips taut the smell of cold
wood and the lull in which you draw your shirt to
your left shoulder • the morning is something
that comes over the crest of the hill vast and
unending in indian red • we ate oranges in the
dark

vathi, 24. 8. 97

Isaac Newton—*Principia*

es war ein dienstag • der weiß gestrichene tisch
und die stühle standen im rasen und ich saß
zum essen mit meinen stiefschwestern • es war warm

und wegen der pest die fakultät geschlossen • ein glas wasser
neben dem teller und der ausgelöste fisch
verursachten ekel mir: der dünne darm

das schwarz gestockte blut • wir sprachen belangloses ihre
münder sah ich lautlos sich bewegen
und hinter ihrem rücken so etwas wie einen flügel

bloß beschnitten an den rändern • ein absichtsloses
streifen fast als wollte ein engel ihre gedanken erwägen dann
fiel ein apfel plötzlich von seinem ast

und die welt war in sich aufgehoben • die hügel
das haus der zaun • kein anfang fand
mehr zum ende an vorbestimmter stelle—er widerstand

seinem natürlichen drang nach ordnung • eine last
lag auf den dingen und von ihrer masse ging eine schwere
aus die sie voneinander abstieß • ins ungefähre

woolsthorpe, 1666

Isaac Newton—*Principia*

it was a tuesday • out on the grass
chairs and the table painted white where i ate
with my stepsisters • it was warm

and the faculty shut for the plague • a glass
of water and the gutted fish upon the plate
were but nauseous to me: that black coagulum

and thin intestine • our talk was idle
i saw them mouthing soundless words
and behind their backs something like a wing

though its edges clipped • as if a passing angel
tried to weigh their thoughts with its caress
then an apple fell and everything

that was the world was held • the gateway
the house the hill • no beginning now could
meet its end at the appointed place—it withstood

such natural urge for order • a burden lay
on things and from their mass there came a gravity
forcing them apart • to indefinity

   woolsthorpe, 1666

Albert Einstein—*Spezielle Relativität*

der kopfbahnhof der vorstadt • die baugerüste
vor den häusern • radfahrer und passanten • im speisewagen

    auf der fahrt nach ulm war das bier billiger als wein und
die teller aus meißner porzellan • ich spürte es im magen

wenn die lok anfuhr und dachte an milevas brüste
der geruch wie von trocknenden hagebutten auf einem stein

    es gibt keine bedeutung des gültigen für entfernung
noch für einen standpunkt • automobile und gehwege • jeder

glaubt an einen ort • als ich ein junge war sah ich
die gesichter in den waggons verzerrt wie in einem konvexen

    spiegel die körper zurückgedrückt in das polsterleder
flach den zug unter dampfschwaden verkürzt: die zeichnung

eines fluchtpunktes aus dem lehrbuch • komplexen
sachverhalten gewann ich meine moral ab • unter dem strich

    bleibt davon bloß der anstand zweier herren im abteil
und wie wir uns mißtrauisch mustern • die einzige konstante

Albert Einstein—*Special Relativity*

a terminal in the suburbs • scaffolding
on the houses • cyclists and pedestrians • in the dining

      car on the way to ulm the beer was cheaper than wine
and the plates of meissen porcelain • i felt it in my stomach

as the engine pulled away and thought of mileva's breasts
the smell of drying rose-hips on a stone

      there is no significance in the validity of distance
or a point of view • automobiles and pavements • everyone

believes in a place • when i was a boy i saw
the faces in railway carriages distorted as if by convex

      mirrors bodies pressed back in upholstered seats
flat the train foreshortened under clouds of steam: the text-
    book

diagram of a vanishing point • i derived my morals from
    complex
states of affairs • what is left is the mere

      decorum of two gentlemen in a compartment
and the way we size each other up • the only constant

ist das licht das die fassaden herunterwäscht steil
und unbeteiligt • jedes andere gerede über eine eigenschaft

       fußt nur auf wahrscheinlichkeiten • an der bettkante
aufzuwachen neben ihr war leicht • aber etwas war vergebens

jemand der im fall begriffen ist spürt die schwerkraft
nicht • das war der glücklichste gedanke eines ganzen lebens

    bern, 1905

is the light that washes down these facades sheer
and indifferent • all rumor of other properties

is based solely on probability • waking beside her
at the edge of the bed was easy • but something

was amiss • someone falling does not feel
gravity's force • the happiest thought of my whole life was this

bern, 1905

La Zisa

und kehrten zurück in den umhegten garten • eden
die gipfel weit um die bucht in der farbe der narzissen
und mitten in diesem saal des sommers der sebihl
eine quelle aus marmor • rippen die kehl um kehl hervortreten
als würde wasser über wasser fließen
um sich in die vier flüsse zu ergießen • es ist still
bäume voll orangen und widergespiegelt auf der fayence
der reglos blauen becken deine silhouette • ein bild
das in sich selbst besteht: diese licht an den tag gelegte absenz
glast • hoch darüber in den kapitellen
pfaue die ihre federn ausstellen • das fleisch unverweslich hielt
ihr rad die sonne in den augen • und zurückstehlen
wollt ich sie dir: das ist es was worte tun • blendarkaden
offene fenster für den wind und einen klaren blick
über kuppeln • in der nische vielleicht
einer der den becher reicht akrobaten schachspieler im mosaik
amphoren im sand über den gewölben im schatten
safranfäden in der hand • etwas das sich dir niederneigt
und weg • alles vollkommne immer nur im werden

grande albergo & delle palme, 4. 1. 01

La Zisa

and we returned to the enclosed garden • eden
the peaks far around the bay in the hues of narcissi
and amid this court of summer the *sebihl*
a marble fountain • ribs rippling one by one
as if water welled on water
to flow into the rivers four • how still it is
trees full of oranges and mirrored in the faience
of the calm blue pools your silhouette • an image
inhering in itself: the lucidity of this absence
agleam • high above on the capitals peacocks spread
their feathers • with imperishable flesh
fans kept the sun in their eyes • i tried
to steal it back for you: that is what words
can do • open windows for the wind blind arcades
and a clear view over cupolas • in that niche perhaps
one offering the cup chess-players in mosaic acrobats
amphorae in the sand over arches in the shade
threads of saffron in the palm • something bowing
to you and then gone • all perfection only ever becoming

    grande albergo & delle palme, 4. 1. 01

Szenen der Jagd XII

zeugenberge • blöcke und brocken glänzend schwarz
tags zuvor hatte ich sie im feldstecher hinaufjagen gesehen
flanke an flanke innehaltend witterung aufnehmen
und wieder weiter durch diesen glast seitwärts

sich schlagend • es waren schwere tiere das auflohen
ihrer mähnen das einzige was sie vom fels abhob
den wind an der wange kletterte ich in diesem abwegsamen
den klüften entlang • geröll das frost gesprengt

und sand zerschliffen hatte und so liegen blieb
in jenem flüchtigen gleichgewicht das eine zeit bedingt
die nicht in atemzügen mißt oder im blut das klopft
ihr ausmaß war diese halde hier • ich kauerte im morgenlicht

regungslos unter einem überhang und wartete
in einer anspannung die nur im ausharren sich erschöpft
glaubte steine gegeneinanderschlagen zu hören ein schnauben
und meinte sie von mir längst schon verscheucht

weil ich den blick dafür verlor sich alles um mich verhärtete
und sah eines davon armlängen vor mir ein horn reiben
an den trümmern • den gelben ring der augen
das fell wie dunkler hafer nein: sand zurückbeugen

Scenes of the Hunt XII

relict mountains • blocks of black and shining
slabs • i'd seen them through binoculars the day before
dash upward flank to flank pause nose to the air
and off again a traverse through the glare

heavy beasts whose flaming manes alone
betrayed them against the rock • wind
on my cheek i climbed in the impassable in ravines
boulders broken by frost ground down by sand

and come to rest in that transient balance
whose scale of time supposed a measure
outwith breaths and throbbing blood
its dimension was this scree • i crouched motionless

in the morning light waiting under an overhang
in a tension only perseverance can exhaust
thought i heard stones crashing a snorting and believed
them long scared off by me because i had lost

my eye for it and around me everything was hardening
and saw it a couple of arms' lengths away
scraping its horn on the ridge • the yellow ring of the eye
its coat like dark oats no: like sand bending back

das genick und den kopf wegneigen • und hielt still
nach wie vor als könnte man diesen moment mit allem
vergangenenen verschränken • dann der nachhall
von hufen im schutt der eine silhouette ausfüllte mit reellem

tin haberti, 11. 1. 02

its neck and turning its head away • and kept as still
as before as if this one moment could interlock
with all things past • then the echo of hooves
in the rubble filling a silhouette with what was real

    tin haberti, 11. 1. 02

Carolina Schutti

The Studio—a sketch

I

She entered his shop without a greeting, determinedly
reached for the things she needed, paid, and left without a
word, just as she had entered. It had been oil colors she used
to buy once in a while. But lately, perhaps since the summer,
she had started to come frequently. She stopped buying paints
and started to buy clay, plaster of Paris and wax, mainly clay
though, the kind which gets lighter in color on drying. The
shop-owner knew a lot of weird characters, eccentric ones,
chatty ones, grumpy ones, and some who smiled all the time.
But no one had eyes like she had. Black, deep. On the few
occasions he could take a look into her eyes at the till, he had
seen this bottomless depth. No shine to reflect some of his
own image. This blackness swallowed up even the daylight.

Most of the time she had her head bowed anyway, but not
out of humility.

II

It was only this summer that they would lie in the sun, talk
about irrelevant things and about important issues. Gret had
wanted to go off somewhere, just the two of them, some place
where they would not understand the language, where nobody
would understand their language, where nobody would know
that one of them made the most of her life, while the other
one had probably failed already. She begged her, but all they

ever did was lie by the lake, Eva didn't want to go anywhere or maybe she couldn't, she was indispensable here or thought she was, she had lain on this very lawn as long as she could remember, was perfectly happy with herself, Gret's face in the shadow that her sister left on the towel. Eva talked, and Gret looked at her with her black eyes and remained silent. Everything she had to say she had put into her pictures—and it wasn't much. So Gret looked at Eva, heard her talk about her talent, about making the right decisions, about her ability to charm people, saw her happy face, keenly felt the shadow on her own and all of a sudden also her own insignificance. Without a word, she got up on this peaceful sunny afternoon, incapable of standing herself in the sparkling vibrancy of the sun, even less capable of not shrinking painfully next to her alter image. She left and Eva did not hear from her again.

III

At the back of the big room some paintings were piled up, covered with gray plastic, coated with a layer of dust. Some brochures of minor galleries lay on top of a shelf, next to them some old brushes and a bunch of keys. There was a washbasin and a mattress and a gas cooker set on a small, cracked table.

Light came in through two skylights and lit the middle of the studio, where, in-between the two strips of light that appeared on the floor at midday, stood an old chair and an equally old easel. Gret knelt on the seat, reabsorbed the colors which she had torn from deep inside her with her eyes, just as if she couldn't release and share them with the eyes of a stranger, she knelt until her knees ached and the strips of light had long disappeared. She squatted in the twilight, waiting until the few strokes on the canvas would turn gray and eventually almost black.

IV

That very evening she began to buy clay. In large blocks, as much as she could carry. She didn't talk to the neighbors for weeks, for months. She left the studio only to shop, she forgot to eat. Her eyes became bigger, but above all lost their luster, she pinched her lips together, her shoulders bowed under the weight of her work. From the street one could see light in the little window every night, only rarely did a shadow cross the square of light.

V

They came for Gret late in the afternoon. The advertising leaflets in front of her door gave her away. The undertakers thought they were carrying away a child—in their faces an expression of incredulous horror. The door to the studio had been locked again, the sister was called. Some days later she was standing in the stairwell. Stunned. She stood there to find an answer. A monumental work. Something Gret had been consumed with. A work that had something to say, maybe even about the silent Gret. She stood there for a long time, in front of the white door, holding the key in her hand. At some point she turned the key in the lock and pushed the door open. Her skin tightened all over her body, her mouth went dry, she clenched her fists, squeezing the key so tight it hurt; Eva saw shelves, shelves from floor to ceiling, on every single wall—filled, overfilled—with her, Eva, made out of non-fired clay, coated with black wax.

Kellstein

The moth was still twitching a bit with its spotted wings. He took a tissue, with the fold between his thumb and forefinger, cautiously pressed the two fingers together, in a way that the insect would not leave stains on the floor. With considerable pressure he crumpled up the tissue, opened the door of the bathroom and, without turning on the light, flushed the dead moth down the toilet. Then he positioned himself in front of the washbasin. For quite a while he kept standing there in the pale light from the hallway 'til he started to soap his hands thoroughly, even though there was no blood on them, and watched the water run down the sink.

Kellstein took off his jacket. For a short moment his look was fixed on the name tag with the company logo, the color of which did not fit the fabric of the jacket. "A. Kellstein." If on a Monday at about eight o'clock he was trying to start a conversation with a woman in the bar, he took off the name tag and introduced himself as Herbert Hochriegel. Despite this—to his mind—promising name, it happened rarely that a woman left the place with him, and if one did, she only stayed for a few hours. It was not because of his grooming—he could have handled that because he could change it any time—it must have something to do with his character, he would not deny any of his traits, and this insight, which he had gained after years, really offended him deeply.

It was on a Thursday. He had to take a taxi because he was too late to catch the tram. He sat down on the backseat and in a genteel voice told the driver where he wanted to go. The taxi driver did not understand him and asked again. On the way across town nothing but celebrities were grinning at Kellstein from the hoardings. Some of them as nondescript as he was, but all of them famous, no one was wearing a name tag. "Look, isn't that …?" "Can I take a picture of you?" "Hi, have a good day." He would react politely, and with a soft smile on his face he would also wish people a good day, and now and then he would give an autograph to someone.

Kellstein, Kellstein. The taxi had arrived, Kellstein paid and went in to take up his place in the company. It was useless to stand upright and put a gentle smile on your face. Nobody remembered his pale face, and hardly anyone wished him a good day.

Even his suit fell in with the rest of him, his tempo to the beat of all the others, his name featureless, his life likewise— except for, yes.

It was on a Thursday. He never went to the bar on Thursday because those evenings already anticipated the weekend, people met, made plans, he would listen to their conversations, let himself get caught up in their excitement and take it home and then he would not know what to do with it. Today, though, he let himself drift.

Straightaway he went to his regular seat. He was not even thinking of his name tag, he left it on his jacket. Now and then his right hand touched his jacket pocket, which contained something with an angular shape, as if to make sure that it was still there or to work up some courage, like when people clutch a lucky charm made of jade or any other lucky stone before an exam.

He ordered a small beer, his left elbow resting on the bar, his feet high above the ground on the foot rest of the barstool. By and by people came in, in twos, in small groups and larger groups. The air was getting thicker and the music louder. Suddenly somebody nudged him from behind. He turned his head around. "Good evening, Mister Kellstein." "How come you know…" "But you're wearing a name tag. Are you working here?" Kellstein was getting embarrassed, he did not say anything and just shook his head. "I don't want to bother you, I was just thinking…I'm staying overnight, on business, and I thought…maybe we could have a chat." This was new. Kellstein was overwhelmed. Someone had addressed him even though he was not sitting upright and not smiling gently. The way he was crouching on the barstool, his legs crossed, one foot even slung round the ankle of the other one. The hair parted, the face not unfriendly, but pale, the eyes never still, the entire body seemed to be self-absorbed, as if strings were tied to the inside of his skin, like fish-hooks that converged in his stomach and were pulled together ever tauter.

"Marta," she said and put out her hand. She was beautiful. Elegant. And she looked intelligent. And she wanted to chat with him. "Kellstein," he answered and pressed her hand. This was new. It must have something to do with his character. Or it was that Marta had an eye for the really distinctive: for things which were not printed on billboards—for secret features, so to speak. She probably had an instinct for such. And he decided to do everything right. Address Marta formally all night long. Show respect for her, and so on. They were chatting for quite a while, but Kellstein took in almost nothing of what she was talking about. Inwardly he was preparing himself for inviting her. He was waiting for the right moment. Because today he would do everything right, no inhibitions, no false bashfulness—and frankness from the start. She should know about his particularity immediately. About a particularity that no one would have guessed. And so, since Marta had nothing better to do and Kellstein seemed harmless to her, while his circumspect behavior and his apparent expertise in cultural matters had allayed her concerns, and since she was also curious about the special recording he would play to her at his home over a glass of wine, she finally went with him.

His flat was simple, but tastefully furnished. The window was open and, as Kellstein switched on the light, he spotted a moth on the wall. Kellstein closed the window, for a moment he was vexed, then he offered Marta a seat. She sat down on a chair, now she felt a bit uneasy after all. "Listen," he said, turning his back on her. She saw him take a CD out of his right jacket pocket. Awkwardly, almost solemnly, he opened its case. Marta was sitting upright, ready to get up at any time. Hardly any sound was coming out of Kellstein's loudspeakers. Just a few scattered piano sounds. He was looking at Marta expectantly. She did not understand. But she politely returned his look. There was someone coughing on the recording and Kellstein instantly stopped the music. "A live-recording. Milan 1992." Marta gave him a questioning look. "The one who is coughing is me. There are no other recordings." Kellstein opened the CD player, took the disk out, put it carefully into the plastic case and then back into his jacket pocket.

For a while no one said anything. Then a sound like a suppressed laugh, the chair being pushed back—and Marta could not restrain herself any longer, she broke out into laughter, shaking her head, perhaps a bit relieved, she put her handbag over her shoulder and left without a word, without looking at Kellstein, and without closing the door. Kellstein did not move. He was standing upright in his suit, the name tag on the right side of his chest, and then after a while he killed the moth, went into the bathroom, took off his suit, and stood there washing his hands.

SEPP MALL

Ein Haus vielleicht

Auf allen Wegen / liegt Schnee
im Atlas der verlorenen Orte
und die Spur / der Kinder-
schuhe
verliert sich
am Waldrand

Vielleicht / taucht noch ein Haus auf
im Nebel
ich gehe den Tieren nach
(ihren dampfenden Rücken)
den Kühen / im Glocken-
gebimmel
setz / meine Schritte
ins Eis (wer weiß)
: vielleicht ruft jemand noch
meinen Namen

A House, perhaps

All the paths are covered / with snow
in the atlas of lost locations
and the trace / of children's
shoes
peters out
near the edge of the woods

Perhaps / a house will emerge
from the fog
I follow the animals
(their steaming backs)
the cows / amid the tinkling of
cow bells
place / my steps
on the ice (who knows)
: maybe someone will call out
my name, eventually

Lichtwechsel (I)

Als wärs ein / und derselbe Ton
: im Klatschen der Wellen
im Schnitt der Sense / im Gras

Und wenn die Säge sich
durchs Holz / frißt
hältst du den Atem an
Und wenn du über dem Gehen
den Abgrund / ahnst

Es ist kein Singen mehr
aber auch kein / Schrei
und ich frage dich
ob es ein Maß gibt / in dem
die Welt schwingt
: ein heiterer Pulsschlag
mitten / im Einerlei

Change of Light (I)

As if it were the / very same sound
: in the slapping of the waves
in the severing of the scythe / in the grass

And when the saw eats
its way through / the wood
you hold your breath
And when you sense the abyss
while / walking

It's no longer a singing
but neither is it / a cry
and I ask you
whether there is a unit / in which
the world oscillates
: a cheerful pulse beating
amidst / the monotony

Last Exit (Kleine Zuversicht)

In solchen Stunden / fiele
das Abschiednehmen
leicht
: Brauchst nur / dem Pochen
der Wälder zu folgen
dem Zug der Wildenten
(über alle Verkehrs-
regeln hinweg)

Oder dem Rade-
brechen / des Herzens

Wenn der Sommer (dir)
bis in den Mund reicht
und dein Haus / geschultert ist
: schnecken-
gleich

Last Exit (Limited Hope)

In such hours / bidding
farewell would be
easy
: you just need to / follow
the pounding of the woods
the migration of wild ducks
(disregarding all
traffic regulations)

Or the trembling
of / the heart

When the summer
reaches into (your) mouth
and your house is / shouldered
: like a snail's
shell

An Vaters Hand

Und trotzdem wars / als
ginge man / mitten im Text
hielte sich fest an den flach
atmenden Sätzen
die ihm das Gras / schrieb
(sein beständiger Wuchs)
oder die / Jahreszeit

Und wenn der Herbst
sein Kapitel / schloß
(von einem Tag auf den andern)
blätterten wir einfach um
(wie wirs / gelernt)
auf eine schneeweiße Seite

Voller Hasenspuren / vor-
sichtiger Tritte
ins Licht

At Father's Hand

And yet it was / as if
you were walking / in the middle of the text
clinging to the shallowly
breathing sentences
which the grass wrote / for him
(its constant growth)
or the / season

And when the autumn
closed / its chapter
(from one day to the next)
we just turned the page
(as we had / learned)
to a snow-white sheet

Full of rabbit tracks / care-
ful steps
into the light

Weiter draußen

In der Gischt fransen die Wörter aus
wie Wolken
im lichten April
und der Wind / treibt
Musik von den Häusern her
Stücke aus zerbrechendem Glas
Hier / kannst du mich berühren
(sagst du)
im Niemandsland
im Gestrüpp / zwischen den Jahren

Lichtwechsel (III)

Im Kammerflimmern / endet
das Jahr
in Wellen bricht die Nacht
über die Dinge / über das
was einem anvertraut

Wir holten Brot / sahen
den Eltern zu
wie sie starben / ver-
jagten die Fliegen

Erklärungen nützen nichts
das Zittern blieb

Farther out

Amid the sea spray the words become frayed
like clouds
in pale April
and the wind / draws out
music from the houses
pieces of shattering glass
here / you can touch me
(you say)
in the no-man's-land
in the brushwood / between the years

Change of Light (III)

In the heart's glimmering ventricle / the year
ends
in waves the night breaks in
over the things / that
you have been entrusted with

We fetched some bread / watched
the parents as
they were dying / swatted
the flies away

Explanations were useless
the trembling remained

das Zucken der Welt
: wie Flügelschlag verendender
Vögel
den (ganzen) Nachmittag über
den kommenden Tag

....

Wo das Blatt / vorm Fenster
im Sturm sich festhielt
und dann doch
: sich fallen läßt
in den Abgrund der Morgenstille

Atemlos / entlang
der Vorstellungsgrenze
: vielleicht / wären das
die Orte der Gedichte
wenn es so etwas
überhaupt gibt / einen

Platz / einen Raum
für Worte

the twitching of the world
: like the wing beat of shrivelling
birds
(all) afternoon long
the following day

....

Where the leaf / in front of the window
clung tightly to itself amid the storm
but finally
: lets itself fall
down into the abyss of morning stillness

Breathless / along
the border of imagination
: maybe / this would be
the poems' territory
if there is anything
as such / a

space / a room
for words

Wechselnde Anschriften (I)

Immer wieder ein Frühling
ein Grün
das ans Licht drängt
und kosende Paare unter Bäumen

Frag mich nicht / was
dauert: wechselnde An-
schriften / verblassende Bilder
manchmal ein Geruch
der sich mitten ins Er-
innern setzt
: von modrigen Haus-
aufgängen / kleinen Zimmern
wo du dich umdrehst
und sagst: wir bleiben

Changing Addresses

Spring, time and time again
a green
thrusting up towards the light
and caressing couples under the trees

Don't ask me / what
will last: changing
addresses / fading images
sometimes a smell
that settles amidst re-
collections
: of moldy stair-
ways / small rooms
where you turn around
and say: here we stay

The Woman with the Bird Mask

Else lies naked and stares into darkness. The window is open. She counts the cars passing by. It's hard to breathe, the sheet under her back is damp. The heat is unbearable. Not even at night does the temperature drop.

The idea of putting a sheet into the freezer comes to her mind. It would offer relief. Later, beneath her skin.

Else prays for a current of air.

Shortly afterwards she jumps out of bed, grabs the sheet from the cupboard and dashes into the kitchen. Water, she thinks, I must drink some water. Else gulps down one glass and then another. Liquid runs down her neck, between her breasts, the last drops seep away in her deep navel.

She staggers back into the bedroom and tries to read. It will take some time for the sheet to cool down. She has wedged it between the ice cream and the fillet of sole; she doesn't want to think about the smell. From her belly she rolls over onto her side, from her side onto her back, from her back onto her other side; she turns the page and puts the book aside. In such a night, when the air is oppressive and weighs down on the body, no one is able to read.

Images flare up, fleeting and bright, only to vanish immediately into nothingness. From far away Else hears voices and laughter. A thought, scarcely grasped, a second one, unfinished, a few smithereens, they come, cluster and dissolve.

Else prays for the throbbing in her head to stop.

No way will she go there.

Else tosses and turns. Wriggles around on the pillow.

Maybe she'd be able to sleep during the day. But she knows she's deceiving herself. Hopes?

Else pulls up her legs and pushes herself around in a circle on the queen-size bed. Armies of men on wooden stilts are marching over her head, thousands rushing forward in lock-step, she senses their thuds and a drum. Lead balls are hurtling towards her, Else lifts her arms, flails around, wanting to ward them off. The sun is merciful, lead melts and drops into a green iris. Future images and a metallic band on the horizon.

Sleeping with open eyes. That would be the way to do it. If only she could manage that. Nothing could ever throw her off track again. But the hours awake leave shadows and creases on her face. An imperceptible shiver in the body.

Of course, she won't go there.

Just says, see you tomorrow. As if he could make decisions. She didn't give him the slightest reason to make him think she'd come back.

Else squirms and twists until she hauls herself up from the mattress. Two more hours, then she'll have to get up. She sees the indentations on the bed, the traces of her restlessness, she wrenches the sheet out; what is it you really want, Else? Sometimes she talks to herself, she has been living on her own for a long time.

Dirty laundry bulges out of a fabric bag, fresh sheets every day, she keeps having to change her clothes. She cannot stand the smell. She climbs into the bathtub, cold water beats down on her forehead, her shoulders, she raises her face into the jet of water. Else remains strict with herself. Discipline and reason are her weapons. Else watches herself in the mirror, her hand casually brushing her thighs, belly, breasts. She isn't twenty anymore, but happy with her figure.

While rubbing herself down with a towel, she lets yesterday's events pass through her mind.

Else wanted to stretch her legs. She waited for the evening. Sometimes, at this time of day, a brisk breeze blows across the town and makes the heat-stricken citizens sigh with relief. She was lucky yesterday, the wind from the valley didn't let her down. Else felt the relief on her neck, under her arms, and how the air rushed into her shirt. She strolled down to the river, the banks parched and dusty. Grasses and leaves and trees, the landscape was coated in brown. No rain for months. Not a single drop.

At the point where she had usually turned back she kept on walking yesterday, she drifted along with the crowd of people who had crawled out of their dwellings. Past the museum and hi-fi shop-windows, aimless and without any idea of what to do with these evening hours. She almost enjoyed not wanting anything, for Else always has an aim and she always wants something.

Else brushes, she massages the oil into her skin in circling movements, from her feet towards her heart. Our bodies talk to us, Else knows that and takes care of hers. The nights are too warm; without the benefit of sleep, without this drifting off they sap her strength. The brushing has stimulated the circulation. Now she feels ready for the challenge again.

She won't go there.

Probably, it's this summer that is wearing her down, taking away her willpower. News agencies are reporting forest fires in the vicinity, the houses are crooked, gables are groaning beneath the roofs, doors and window shutters are warping, pigeons are falling from the sky, perishing in the softened tarmac and, if you listen closely, you can hear the town emitting a high-pitched, desperate hum.

Voices wafted over from the town square. Laughter. Else saw a circle of spectators, she came closer, stood on tiptoe, A group of performers!, she had read about it.

A feathered girl was standing, motionless, on a cube. She was covered in gold from head to toe, the whites of her eyes the only sign of life. She rewarded those who threw her coins with a quarter or half turn. A man was tottering on stilts through the crowd, juggling with balls or abruptly bending his knees, people scattering in all directions. He pulled a face. Else wondered whether pulling faces was healthy.

A red-haired woman stepped out of the tent, a python dangling from her neck, her body wrapped in a yellow-white overall. She was older than the other performers, the painted eyes seemed tired. Snake and woman, together they resembled an ugly multi-tentacled jellyfish. Else remembered the fact that the reticulated python lays up to a hundred eggs. It's the only snake that hatches them itself. The man on stilts made the balls disappear, he grabbed a piece of wire and teased the python. It moved, the red-haired woman staggered under the wavelike movement. When he pursed his lips, the serpent shot out into his face. The audience screamed, the man jumped down from the stilts and bowed. When he straightened up, Else caught his gaze. He looked her in the eye. For minutes, it seemed. As if he wanted to form a judgment.

Unexpectedly, he thrust the heel of his leather boot into the asphalt, turned around and, while passing, bit the jellyfish in the shoulder. The red-haired woman gave him a worn-out smile. Else discerned scars under the running make-up. The pair of them disappeared hand in hand under the tarpaulin.

Else was about to start her way back home when the people whistled. The man jumped forward, he had a belt around his belly. Without hesitation, he homed in on Else, pulled her from the back row into the middle and asked her to check what he had with him. No, Else warded him off, she didn't care for knives. The man grasped her arm so hard that it hurt. He kept staring at her. Else had to avert her gaze.
At that he carelessly let go of her arm and began to sharpen the blades.

Else thought all this was silly.

A cardboard partition on wheels appeared, and walking behind it a graceful figure; she was wearing a beaked mask, dark red silk was flowing down her body. Probably the jellyfish woman, Else could only assume so, as the hair was hidden under the hood.

Give me your hand!

As Else didn't move, the man took her hand, turned the palm upside, pulled her sleeve back and softly stroked down her arm.

Else's shoulders relaxed. Her throat was dry.

His face gave nothing away.

Suddenly she heard a snapping sound. The man pushed something hard-edged against the place he had touched and kept his eye on Else. She felt the pain. Her heart was beating hard. Suddenly, she wished the stranger were pulling silver through her flesh.

The man smiled, for a moment she saw his tongue, the ring. He let go of her and said, see you tomorrow. As if it were a foregone conclusion.

Else pushed through the crowd, using her elbows and hips. She ran upstream, got out of breath, swallowed dust and dried clover.

At home she threw herself onto the bed. Desperately longing for sleep. But the night robbed it from her and felt like an animal in gestation.

Meanwhile, Else has dressed. She puts the oil and the brush into the wire basket, does things she can't remember later. Else shops, Else drinks tea and listens to the news, Else makes phone calls, writes the article for next week's issue of *The Ritalin Society*, Else cooks, eats, browses through newspapers, Else lies down with open eyes, feeds the neighbors' cats, they always need to go off somewhere, Kilimanjaro, Mount Everest, Else takes a shower, slices bread, cuts chives…

Eventually, silence falls. A silence that seeps from the walls, from the furniture, from the dishes standing around. What do you want from him, Else speaks against the silence, nothing. Or something after all. Less loneliness. For a short while. A new body. Someone who isn't sparing with his life. A little danger. Memories. The hope of a later autumn. Don't make a fool of yourself. Your autumn is coming anyway. Their situations are too different. A man on stilts. A knife-thrower. What have you got to lose? Your market value is falling, you're not getting any younger and prettier. You should ask yourself whether you're happy. Your sister claims that your laugh has a bitter undertone. Why this detachment? Can't you forget yourself for once, Else? Let yourself go. What are you afraid of? Else hears her echo. The rooms are sparsely furnished. She hates lavishness.

She wants to conjure up his picture, the bald head, the bristling brows, the mouth, movements which suggest casualness or arrogance.

The air in the apartment is stifling.

Else dabs at her upper lip with a kitchen towel. She pulls the drawer out, takes the kitchen knife, lays metal onto her forehead. The coolness is pleasant. She looks at her watch, maybe, if she hurried. She tries on half a dozen different outfits, discarding them all, too formal, too nondescript, too provocative, too baggy, until she goes for the simple alternative, a top and Bermuda shorts.

Else hears her own steps, as if they had nothing to do with herself, she takes the shortest way from her door to the square. While running, she pulls off her sandals, carries them by their straps. Passers-by look at her with curiousity, who might be hurrying like that after office hours and barefoot at that. Else doesn't care.

The tent is there. But nothing else. No show. People strolling about and children playing. Else slips into her sandals, she is relieved that the tarpaulin is still there. For a moment Else is undecided. What now?

Swiftly she slips into the tent.

The man is sitting with his back towards the entrance. He's straddling a wooden bench, his head bowed. He seems to be feeding someone. Else's trying to control her rapid heartbeat, to be quiet, but he has already noticed her.

I have been expecting you.

Else blushes. The color washes from her face to her neckline.

You liked it, didn't you? He casually turns his torso and leg over the wooden bench in a wide circle. Else hopes that her embarrassment remains invisible in the twilight. She looks at her toes, at the mats on the floor, not at him, she doubts whether she'd be able to avert her gaze.

What are you doing? Else asks.

The man reaches behind his back and puts a hairy bundle onto his six-pack. One leg bent, the other stretched out, he supports himself with one arm. A mouse opossum, he says. Else notices the bat-like ears, the naked tail and the pink mouth. His fingers dig into the fur, the creature lets out a piercing cry. Else thinks, it's laughing at me.

An insatiable one. Devours vermin without chewing. It hunts after nightfall. At these words, he's staring at Else again.

The python!, where's the python, it could be slithering around right here, in a single bound and with a muted scream,

Else leaps onto the bench.

As quick as a flash the man embraces her knees. He lifts his scruffy chin and smirks, what is it that frightens the unapproachable woman?

Else is at a loss. Why unapproachable? What does he know of her life? She wants to get down to the floor, but he keeps hugging her legs. Behind the wild brows, behind the stubble and the coarse features she suddenly discovers his softer traits. The man lifts Else up, plants her on the floor in front of a glass case.

The python's forked tongue is shooting back and forth. Under its yellow gaze a bunch of spider lilies is dying.

He's now holding a lighter, touches his palms with the flame, passes his fingers through it, lights the stump of a candle. He gets tobacco and cigarette paper out of his shirt pocket. He's sure to take deep pulls, Else thinks. The man inhales deeply and slowly. Then he puts a blindfold around his head, tying the ends together, he murmurs, I can eat fire, do you want me to show you?

Else can no longer refrain from saying: Why are you being such a show-off?

Why are you here? He smiles as if he were enjoying himself.

Yes, why? What was this supposed to be?

Else wants to get out. Away from the fuss. She turns to leave, when suddenly he's holding her in his arms.

You shall never fear anything again, while he's whispering, he gently slips a strand of hair behind her ear.

What does he mean by that? That is. That would also be. An aim, if you wanted to see it that way. That would be … What if she slips off? Breaks off? Loses the picture?

Else prays for the throbbing in her head to stop.

Meanwhile, the man has fetched some silk from a box, he puts the mask on her head, the beak pointing skywards, Else thinks, only a tent roof separates me from the sky and I am the woman with the bird mask.

The robe has no shoulders, the sleeves are bell-shaped, he lets the dark red ocean flow down over Else's skin, her back, Else smells both bodies, as they struggle to breathe against the heat, the man whispers words into her ear.

He takes a plastic box, begins to apply make-up, he strives for perfection, maybe he is more like her than she has assumed, he spreads the porcelain white, forehead, nose, neck, kneeling he dabs at her bare feet.

All of a sudden, he grabs Else, pushes her back, her spine hits something hard. The resistance yields, Else staggers, the man kicks at wheels, at pedals. The partition stands firm. He fumbles for her arms, forces them up, rubs them raw, fastens her joints with strings. Here, there, don't you move!

Else hangs from the hooks, she lets it all happen.

The man gazes at her with eyes wide open. A knife snaps open, the steel presses against her sternum, Else twitches to the side, at the same time his mouth is coming closer, the ring hits the teeth.

Let me throw knives, chase the fear out of your body.

Else swallows, a fatherly voice drifts up from her

childhood, Do not play with knives, you could get hurt.

The circus man caresses Else, he takes his time, one of his hands glides down between her legs, he fixes her with his gaze. Else remembers the scarred half-face, a fleeting picture. She feels the burning, the excitement and his body, as it's pressing against hers. There's no story, no beginning, no ending, only outlines, a dazzling white light, the here and now. The man caresses and moistens his fingers, the fingertips, he has probably released one hand, she thinks, weightlessness is overcoming Else, red waves are washing her away, she can't see the shore anymore... until she realizes that the man is pulling silver through her fingertips.

Else screams.

The man unties her immediately. You wanted it! It fascinated you.

Else screams.

Well, forget it then, the man steps back, his soles touching the rush mats. He swings his arm back, takes possession of the space, hurls the flick-knife at the partition, where it vibrates, dies away. He pulls his hands up with playful resignation.

Too bad, he says, you'll never know.

What...? Her voice is choking.

The singing of the knives, he murmurs.

Else's lower lip is trembling. The man leaves the tent.

Enraged, she snatches the mask off her face, pulls the robe off her body, it would have been her finale, walking away had always been her speciality, he won't grant her the smallest triumph.

Everything around her starts to flicker, she runs blindly through strips of cloth, outside she trips over a child on roller skates. Else mutters, sorry. The sky is pitch black and windless. She feels her make-up running. The child and Else get up, move in the same direction. Towards the closest source of light. Else thinks, what is a child doing here at this time of night, until she hears someone calling, Kati, come here!

Kati, well-behaved, turns back, Kati listens to her father.

Else looks at the floor, sees something curved, feathery and torn. A pigeon is stuck to the surface of the tar, bloodied.

Else closes her eyes, tilts back her head.

She can clearly hear the high-pitched, desperate hum, which has been driving the town crazy for days, for weeks.

Authors' Biographies

Christoph W. Bauer was born in 1968 in Kolbnitz, Carinthia and lives in Innsbruck. He has written poetry, prose, drama, essays and translated texts. He is the recipient of an Ingeborg Bachmann Prize (2001), the Innsbruck Poetry Award (2002), an Austrian State Scholarship for Literature (2002), and two Rome Stipends (2004, 2005).

He published the novels *Der Buchdrucker der Medici* (2009), *Als Kind war ich weise* (2009), *Graubart Boulevard* (2008), *Im Alphabet der Häuser* (2007), and the poetry collection, *die mobilität des wassers müsste man mieten können* (2001), all published by the Haymon Verlag in Innsbruck.

Sabine Gruber was born in 1963 in Merano and grew up in Lana (Northern Italy). She studied German Studies, History, and Political Science at the University of Innsbruck. She taught German at the University of Cà Foscari in Venice (1988-1992) and has been a professional writer since 2000. She lives in Vienna and has written poetry, short fiction, radio and stage plays as well as essays and newspaper commentary. Her plays have aired on Austrian and Italian radio. She has been organizing and editing with Renate Mumelter, the private papers of the South Tyrolese author Anita Pichler; she has edited and published on Pichler.

She published the novels *Aushäusige* (1996) with *Wieser Verlag* in Klagenfurt; *Die Zumutung* (2003) and *Über Nacht* (2007), *Stillbach oder Die Sehnsucht* (2011), all published by C.H. Beck in Munich, and the poetry collection *Fang oder Schweigen* (2002) with *Wieser Verlag* in Klagenfurt.

She has been the recipient of numerous literary awards: City Poet of Klagenfurt (1994), City Poet of Innsbruck (2001), Literary Award for Young Author from the City of Vienna (1996), the Reinhard Priessnitz Prize (1998), Austrian State Prize for Literature (2000), Heinrich Heine Award of the City of Lüneburg (2002), Elias Canetti Prize of the City of Vienna (2004/5), Walther von der Vogelweide Prize (2007), Anton-Wildgans-Prize (2007), Book-Prize of the City of Linz (2008).

Barbara Hundegger was born in Hall in Tyrol in 1963. She studied German Studies, Philosophy, and Drama in Innsbruck and Vienna. She has been working with various women centers organizing projects for women, including literary, cultural, and political events. She has worked as a copy editor, free-lance journalist and writer in Innsbruck.

She published *und in den schwestern schlafen vergessene dinge: Poesie* with Wieser Verlag (1998), *desto leichter die mädchen und alles andre als das: gedichte* in das-fröhliche-wohnzimmer-edition (2002), *kein schluss bleibt auf der andern. nutte nonne lesbe – drei mal raten zählen bis drei*, a drama text for three women, best friend and female choir with Skarabaeus (2004), performed in the Austrian Radio and Television kulturhaus tirol in Innsbruck (2003). *rom sehen und april 05: gedicht-bericht* with Skarabaeus (2006), and poetry in: *stadtstiche – dorfskizzen*, edited by Brigitte Messner with Skarabaeus (2005).

Ulrike Längle was born in 1953 in Bregenz, Vorarlberg. She studied German and Romance Studies at the Universities of Innsbruck and Poitiers, France; she is the director of the Franz-Michel-Felder Archives, the Vorarlberg Literary Archives in Bregenz; she is a writer, literary scholar, and critic. She published *Am Marterpfahl der Irokesen: Liebesgeschichten* (1992), and *Der Untergang der „Romanshorn:" Erzählung* (1994), *Tynne: Novelle* (1996), *Vermutungen über die*

Liebe in einem fremden Haus: Roman (1998), all with S. Fischer in Frankfurt, and *Il Prete Rosso: Zwei Erzählungen* (1996) with Residenz Verlag in Salzburg.

Sepp Mall was born in Graun in South Tyrol, Northern Italy. He is a high school teacher in Merano, South Tyrol; he has been writing poetry, prose, and radio plays since 1971, and was awarded literary prizes in competitions by the South Tyrolese Association of Artitsts (1977 and 1981), the City of Innsbruck (1990), and he also received the Poetry Prize of the city of Meran (1996).

He published *Läufer im Park: Gedichte* (1992) with Haymon in Innsbruck, *Verwachsene Wege: Erzählung* (1993), *Brüder: Erzählung* (1996), *Landschaft mit Tieren unter Sträuchern hingeduckt: Gedichte* (1998), *Wundränder* (2004).

Kerstin I. Mayr was born in 1978 in Innsbruck and studied German and English/American Studies at the University of Innsbruck; she also graduated with a degree in Secondary English Education from City College of New York; she was a fellow at the Brenner Research Archives in Literature of the University of Innsbruck and worked as adjunct faculty for the Teacher Education and School Research Institute of the University of Innsbruck; she is also working as a high school teacher.

Friederike Mayröcker was born in 1924 in Vienna and has been a life long resident of that city; she also took lasting impressions from her stays in the village of Deinzendorf during the first decade of her life. She studied at a junior business college, and then English, and taught English in a secondary school before World War II. She wrote her first text in 1946 and began publishing texts in 1954; in 1956 she began a lifelong friendship with the poet Ernst Jandl; her first poems were published in the avantgarde journal *Plan* and her first book was published in 1956; she has written poetry, prose, stories, radio plays, children's books, and drama ever since.

She published *Die Abschiede* (1980), *Magische Blätter* (1983), *Reise durch die Nacht* (1984), *Das Herzzerreißende der Dinge* (1985), *brütt oder Die seufzenden Gärten* (1998), *Requiem für Ernst Jandl* (2001), *Gesammelte Prosa 1949-2001* (5 vols.); numerous poetry collections, among them *Tod durch Musen* (1966), *Notizen auf einem Kamel* (1996), *Benachbarte Metalle* (1998), *Mein Arbeitstirol* (2003); between 1967 and 1971, she published a number of radio plays, among them with Ernst Jandl *Fünf Mann Menschen* (1968), which received the Prize of the War Blind Association.

She is the recipient of numerous literary awards: Österreichischer Würdigungspreis (1975); Prize of the City of Vienna (1976), Georg-Trakl-Prize (with Reiner Kunze) (1977), Anton-Wildgans-Prize (1982), The Great Austrian State Award (1982), Roswitha-von-Gandersheim-Prize (1982), Honorary Medal in Gold by the Federal Capital Vienna (1985), Honorary Award for Science and the Arts of the Republic of Austria (1987), Erich-Nossack-Prize (1989), Friedrich-Hölderlin-Prize (1993), „manuskripte"-Prize by the State of Styria (1994), Great Literature Award by the Bavarian Academy of the Arts (1996), Else-Lasker-Schüler-Prize (1996), Droste-Prize of the City of Meersburg (1997), America Award Prize (1997), Georg-Büchner-Prize (2001), Karl-Sczuka-Prize (2001), Premio Internazionale (2003).

Claudia Paganini was born in Innsbruck in 1978; she studied Theology and Philosophy at the University of Innsbruck and graduated *sub auspiciis presidentis Rei Publicae* (summa cum laude) in 2004; she published her first novel, short stories, and a volume of poetry during her student days and works as a nonfiction author and as a researcher at the Department of Christian Philosophy at the University of Innsbruck.

Raoul Schrott was born in Tyrol in 1964; he studied Literature and Linguistics in Norwich, Paris, Berlin, and Innsbruck; in 1986/87 he worked as a personal secretary to Philippe Soupault; from 1990 to 1993 he was a lecturer in German Studies at the Instituto Orientale in Naples, Italy; he completed his post-doctoral *Habilitation* in Comparative Literature at the University of Innsbruck in 1997; he lives in Vorarlberg.

He published his University of Innsbruck dissertation *Dada 1921-1922 in Tirol* (1988), *Finis Terrae. Ein Nachlass, Hotels* (1995) with Haymon Verlag in Innsbruck; *Tropen:* Über das Erhabene (1988), a translation of *Gilgamesh* (2001), *Tristan da Cunha oder Die Hälfte der Erde* (2003), the poetry collection, *Weißbuch: Gedichte* (2004), a collection of essays, *Handbuch der Wolkenputzerei* (2005), *Homers Heimat. Der Kampf um Troja und seine realen Hintergründe* (2008), as well as a new translation and literary adaptation of Homer's *Iliad* (2008), all with Carl Hanser Verlag in Munich.

He is the recipient of the following awards and prizes: the Award of the state of Carinthia at the Ingeborg-Bachmann-Competition (1994), Leonce-and-Lena-Prize (1995), Literary Prize of the City of Rauris (1996), the sponsorship award of the Friedrich-Hölderlin-Prize (1996), Berlin Literary Award (1996), Peter-Huchel-Poetry-Prize (1999), City Writer of the city of Mainz (2004), Joseph-Breitbach-Prize (2004), Prize of the Guntram and Irene Rinke Foundation (2007).

Carolina Schutti was born in Innsbruck in 1976; she studied German and English/American Studies at the University of Innsbruck and concert guitar at the conservatory; she wrote her PhD thesis on Elias Canetti; she was a lecturer of German in Florence and at the University of Innsbruck, and taught in a high school; she is on the board of the Brenner-Forum and the Brenner Literary Archives of the University of Innsbruck; she is a literary critic and short story writer.

She published *Die Bibel in Canettis Blendung: Eine Studie zur Intertextualität mit einem Verzeichnis der Bibelstellen* (2006) with innsbruck university press, and the novel *Wer getragen wird, braucht keine Schuhe* (2010) with Otto Müller Verlag in Salzburg.

Birgit Unterholzner was born in 1971 in Bozen in the South Tyrol region of Northern Italy; she studied German Studies, Contemporary History and Media Studies at the University of Innsbruck; from 2001 to 2003 she enrolled in a special course on the pedagogy of theater; she has worked as a high school teacher and consultant in theater pedagogy, and lives as a writer in Bozen.

She published *Die Blechbüchse* (2006) with Skarabäus in Innsbruck, and the novel *Flora Beriot* (2010) with edition laurin of innsbruck university press.

Acknowledgments

Christoph W. Bauer's *atemsprachen, kaum heimgefunden* is from the collection *und wieder rasten die felder* and is an original contribution to this collection.

Sabine Gruber's *Leaves/Blätter* was first published in 2005 in *Die Welt, an der ich schreibe*, ed. by Kurt Neumann, and is published here with the permission of the Sonderzahl-Verlag in Vienna.

Barbara Hundegger's poem *at z. from your balcony/auf z. von deinem balkon aus* was first published in 2005 in: *stadtstiche dorfskizzen* and is published here with the permission of the Skarabaeus Verlag Innsbruck/Wien/Bozen; the poem *pendulum.deflection.result / pendel,ausschlag.befund* was first published in 1998 in : *und in den schwestern schlafen vergessene dinge gedichte* and is published here with the permission of the Wieser Verlag Klagenfurt/Celovec; the poem *family album 1 &2 / familienalbum 1 & 2* was first published in 2002 in: *desto leichter die mädchen und alles andre als das gedichte* (Edition *Das-fröhliche-Wohnzimmer*) and is published here with the permission of Barbara Hundegger.

Ulrike Längle's slightly revised *The Sinking of the "Romanshorn"/ Der Untergang der „Romanshorn"* is from *Der Untergang der „Romanshorn": Erzählungen* (1994), and is published here with the permission of the S. Fischer Verlag in Frankfurt.

Sepp Mall's poem, *A house, perhaps/Ein Haus vielleicht,* was published in *Wo ist dein Haus* (2007); *Change of Light/Lichtwechsel (III),* in *Landschaft mit Tieren unter Sträuchern hingeduckt* (1998), and *Where the leaf, Changing Addresses/Wo das Blatt, Wechselnde Anschriften (I)* are all published here with the permission of the Haymon Verlag in Innsbruck.

Kerstin I. Mayr's poems *wind, under the open sky, Cine Mental/wind. unter freiem himmel. Kopfkino* are original contributions to this collection.

Friederike Mayröcker's *Dream Lines/Traum Linien: Gedicht in Prosa (2), Lamentationen* is an original contribution to this collection.

Claudia Paganini's short story *Golden Mountains/Hüttenzauber* is an original contribution to this collection.

Raoul Schrott's texts *La Zisa/La Zisa* and *Scenes of the Hunt XII/ Szenen der Jagd XII* are in: Weißbuch (2004); *Physical Optics I/ Physikalische Optik I, A History of Writing II/Eine Geschichte der Schrift II, Graukogel/Graukogel, Twilight Phenomena II/ Dämmerungserscheinungen II, Isaac Newton—Principia/Isaac Newton—Principia, Albert Einstein—Special Relativity/Albert Einstein—Spezielle Relativität* are all from *Tropen: Über das Erhabene* (1998), and are all published with the permission of the Hanser Verlag in Munich.

Carolina Schutti's short prose texts *The Studio–a sketch/Das Atelier, eine Skizze* is an original contribution to this collection; *Kellstein/ Kellstein* was first published in *Fluchträume: Lyrik und Prosa* (2006), and is published with the permission of Turmbund in Innsbruck.

Birgit Unterholzner's *The Woman with the Bird Mask/Die Schnabelfrau* is an original contribution to this collection.

Also Available from
PRESS

General Titles

Sometimes Courage Looks Like Crazy: A Journalist's Story by Kim Bondy, 978-1-60801-058-5 (2011)

Post-Katrina Brazucas: Brazilian Immigrants in New Orleans by Annie Gibson, 978-1-60801-070-7 (2011)

The Saratoga Collection, edited by Terrence Sanders, 978-1-60801-061-5 (2011)

The Garden Path: The Miseducation of a City, by Andre Perry, 978-1-60801-048-6 (2011)

Before (During) After: Louisiana Photographers Visual Reactions to Hurricane Katrina, edited by Elizabeth Kleinveld, 978-1-60801-023-3 (2010)

Beyond the Islands by Alicia Yánez Cossío, translated by Amalia Gladhart, 978-1-60801-043-1 (2010)

Writer in Residence: Memoir of a Literary Translator by Mark Spitzer, 978-1-60801-020-2 (2010)

The Fox's Window by Naoko Awa, translated by Toshiya Kamei, 978-1-60801-006-6 (2010)

Black Santa by Jamie Bernstein, 978-1-60801-022-6 (2010)

Dream-crowned (Traumgekrönt) by Rainer Maria Rilke, translated by Lorne Mook, 978-1-60801-041-7 (2010)

Voices Rising II: More Stories from the Katrina Narrative Project edited by Rebeca Antoine, 978-0-9706190-8-2 (2010)

Rowing to Sweden: Essays on Faith, Love, Politics, and Movies by Fredrick Barton, 978-1-60801-001-1 (2010)

Dogs in My Life: The New Orleans Photographs of John Tibule Mendes, 978-1-60801-005-9 (2010)

New Orleans: The Underground Guide by Michael Patrick Welch & Alison Fensterstock, 978-1-60801-019-6 (2010)

Understanding the Music Business: A Comprehensive View edited by Harmon Greenblatt & Irwin Steinberg, 978-1-60801-004-2 (2010)

The Gravedigger by Rob Magnuson Smith, 978-1-60801-010-3 (2010)

Portraits: Photographs in New Orleans 1998-2009 by Jonathan Traviesa, 978-0-9706190-5-1 (2009)

I hope it's not over, and good-by: Selected Poems of Everette Maddox by Everette Maddox, 978-1-60801-000-4 (2009)

Theoretical Killings: Essays & Accidents by Steven Church, 978-0-9706190-6-8 (2009)

Voices Rising: Stories from the Katrina Narrative Project edited by Rebeca Antoine, 978-0-9728143-6-2 (2008)

On Higher Ground: The University of New Orleans at Fifty by Dr. Robert Dupont, 978-0-9728143-5-5 (2008)

The Change Cycle Handbook by Will Lannes, 978-0-9728143-9-3 (2008)

Us Four Plus Four: Eight Russian Poets Conversing translated by Don Mager, 978-0-9706190-4-4 (2008)

The El Cholo Feeling Passes by Fredrick Barton, 978-0-9728143-2-4 (2003)

A House Divided by Fredrick Barton, 978-0-9728143-1-7 (2003)

William Christenberry: Art & Family by J. Richard Gruber, 978-0-9706190-0-6 (2000)

The Neighborhood Story Project

New Orleans in 19 Movements by Thurgood Marshall Early College High School, 978-1-60801-069-1 (2011)

The Combination by Ashley Nelson, 978-1-60801-055-4 (2010)

The House of Dance and Feathers: A Museum by Ronald W. Lewis by Rachel Breunlin & Ronald W. Lewis, 978-0-9706190-7-5 (2009)

Beyond the Bricks by Daron Crawford & Pernell Russell, 978-1-60801-016-5 (2010)

Aunt Alice Vs. Bob Marley by Kareem Kennedy, 978-1-60801-013-4 (2010)

Signed, The President by Kenneth Phillips, 978-1-60801-015-8 (2010)

Houses of Beauty: From Englishtown to the Seventh Ward by Susan Henry, 978-1-60801-014-1 (2010)

Coming Out the Door for the Ninth Ward edited by Rachel Breunlin, 978-0-9706190-9-9 (2006)

Cornerstones: Celebrating the Everyday Monuments & Gathering Places of New Orleans edited by Rachel Breunlin, 978-0-9706190-3-7 (2008)

The Engaged Writes Series

Medea and Her War Machines by Ioan Flora, translated by Adam J. Sorkin, 978-1-60801-067-7 (2011)

Together by Julius Chingono and John Eppel, 978-1-60801-049-3 (2011)

Vegetal Sex (O Sexo Vegetal) by Sergio Medeiros, translated by Raymond L.Bianchi, 978-1-60801-046-2 (2010)

*Wounded Days (Los Días Heridos) by Leticia Luna, translated by Toshiya Kamei, 978-1-60801-042-4 (2010)

When the Water Came: Evacuees of Hurricane Katrina by Cynthia Hogue & Rebecca Ross, 978-1-60801-012-7 (2010)

*A Passenger from the West by Nabile Farès, translated by Peter Thompson, 978-1-60801-008-0 (2010)

*Everybody Knows What Time It Is by Reginald Martin, 978-1-60801-011-0 (2010)

*Green Fields: Crime, Punishment, & a Boyhood Between by Bob Cowser, Jr., 978-1-60801-018-9 (2010)

*Open Correspondence: An Epistolary Dialogue by Abdelkébir Khatibi and Rita El Khayat, translated by Safoi Babana-Hampton, Valérie K. Orlando, Mary Vogl, 978-1-60801-021-9 (2010)

Gravestones (Lápidas) by Antonio Gamoneda, translated by Donald Wellman, 978-1-60801-002-8 (2009)

Hearing Your Story: Songs of History and Life for Sand Roses by Nabile Farès translated by Peter Thompson, 978-0-9728143-7-9 (2008)

The Katrina Papers: A Journal of Trauma and Recovery by Jerry W. Ward, Jr., 978-0-9728143-3-1 (2008)

Contemporary Poetry

California Redemption Values by Kevin Opstedal, 978-1-60801-066-0 (2011)

Atlanta Poets Group Anthology: The Lattice Inside by Atlanta Poets Group, 978-1-60801-064-6 (2011)

Makebelieve by Caitlin Scholl, 978-1-60801-056-1 (2011)

Dear Oxygen: New and Selected Poems by Lewis MacAdams, edited by Kevin Opstedal, 978-1-60801-059-2 (2011)

Only More So by Tony Lopez, 978-1-60801-057-8 (2011)

Enridged by Brian Richards, 978-1-60801-047-9 (2011)

A Gallery of Ghosts by John Gery, 978-0-9728143-4-8 (2008)

The Ezra Pound Center for Literature

The Poets of the Sala Capizucchi (I Poeti della Sala Capizucchi) edited by Caterina Ricciardi and John Gery, 978-1-60801-068-4 (2011)

Trespassing, by Patrizia de Rachewiltz, 978-1-60801-060-8 (2011)

*The Imagist Poem: Modern Poetry in Miniature edited by William Pratt, 978-0-9728143-8-6 (2008)

Contemporary Austrian Studies

Global Austria: Austria's Place in Europe and the World, Günter Bischof, Fritz Plasser (Eds.), Alexander Smith, Guest Editor, 978-1-60801-062-2 (2011)

From Empire to Republic: Post-World-War-I Austria Volume 19 edited by Günter Bischof, Fritz Plasser and Peter Berger, 978-1-60801-025-7 (2010)

The Schüssel Era in Austria Volume 18 edited by Günter Bischof & Fritz Plasser, 978-1-60801-009-7 (2009)

*Also available as E-book